PRACTICE BOOK

Grade 5

Macmillan McGraw-Hill

New York • Farmington

Macmillan/McGraw-Hill

A Division of The **McGraw·Hill** Companies

Illustration by Learning Design Associates.

Macmillan/McGraw-Hill
1221 Avenue of the Americas
New York, New York 10020

Printed in the United States of America

ISBN 0-02-181189-X/5

10 11 12 13 14 15 16 17 18 DBH 05 04 03 02 01 00

Contents

Level 11

UNIT 2: WORLDS OF CHANGE

UNIT 3: WINNING ATTITUDES

UNIT 4: GETTING TO KNOW YOU

UNIT 5: TAKE THE HIGH ROAD

Grandma Essie's Covered Wagon

Klondike Fever

My Adventures at the Center of the Earth

The Silent Lobby

UNIT 6: ZOOM IN!

How to Think Like a Scientist

The News About Dinosaurs

Einstein Anderson

Willie Bea and the Time the Martians Landed

WORDS IN CONTEXT

Complete this passage with vocabulary words.

hoisted   bordered

treacherous   shoreline

astonished   anchor

Ship's Log   Friday, August 26

   No one could be more _____ than I am that we made it.

But here we are safe at _____, in a peaceful harbor

_____ by a sandy _____. It is hard to believe

that less than an hour before, rough seas had nearly _____

our boat onto a _____, rocky reef.

FEELING YOUR WAY THROUGH A STORY

A writer creates mood to help readers experience what the characters in a story are feeling or experiencing. A mood can be created by the story's dialog, descriptions, and actions. Read each of the following passages from "The Wreck of the *Zephyr*." Then describe the mood of the passage.

1. The wind whistled in the rigging as the *Zephyr* pounded her way through the water. The sky grew black and the waves rose up like mountains. The boy struggled to keep his boat from going over.

Mood: _____

2. He climbed a hill, expecting to see something familiar, but what he saw instead was a strange and unbelievable sight. Before him were two boats, sailing high above the water. Astonished, he watched them glide by.

Mood: _____

3. He waited until the sailor and his wife were asleep, then he quietly dressed and went to the harbor. As he rowed out to the *Zephyr*, the boy felt the light evening wind grow stronger and colder.

Mood: _____

4. Then, suddenly, the boy felt the *Zephyr* begin to shake. The sound of the water rushing past the hull grew louder. The air filled with spray as the boat sliced through the waves. The bow slowly began to lift. Higher and higher the *Zephyr* rose out of the water.

Mood: _____

5. The wind blew very hard, churning the sea below. But that did not matter to the *Zephyr* as she glided through the night sky. When clouds blocked the boy's view of the stars, he trimmed the sails and climbed higher. Surely the men of the island never dared fly so high.

Mood: _____

2   Extension: Have students underline the details in each passage that help set the mood.

Level 11/Unit 1
ANALYZE STORY ELEMENTS: Mood   5

Macmillan/McGraw-Hill

WHO, WHAT, WHERE, AND WHEN

The **setting** of a story is where and when the events take place. The setting often has an effect on the characters. Think about how the boy in "The Wreck of the *Zephyr*" was affected by his experiences on the strange island. Answer each question below.

Setting: years ago, in the village

1. The boy says that he is the greatest sailor there is and laughs as he hoists his sails into a blustery wind. What do the boy's words and actions say about his character?

   _____

2. What did the boy always want to prove to the villagers? _____

Setting: the mysterious island

3. What unbelievable and wondrous sight did the boy see at the island?

   _____

4. The boy says he will not leave until he learns how to sail above the waves. What do the boy's words say about his character? _____

5. The boy sneaks out of the sailor's house to try to fly his boat. What does the boy's action say about his character? _____

6. The boy decides to fly over the village and ring the *Zephyr*'s bell. What does the boy's decision say about his character? _____

7. What happens when the boy tries to fly over the village? _____

   _____

Setting: back in the village, after the crash

8. How has the boy's stay on the strange island affected the rest of his life?

   _____

   _____

8

Level 11/Unit 1
ANALYZE STORY ELEMENTS:
Character, Setting

Extension: Have students think about the character of the old man. Knowing that the old man and the boy are probably the same person, have the class discuss how the old man's character might have changed from the boy's, if at all.

3

WHAT'S IT ALL ABOUT?

The **theme** of a story is its overall subject and meaning. Read each passage below from "The Wreck of the *Zephyr.*" Then answer each question to help you uncover the story's theme.

Already a strong wind was blowing. "I'm not afraid," the boy said, "because I'm the greatest sailor there is." The fisherman pointed to a sea gull gliding overhead. "There's the only sailor who can go out on a day like this." The boy just laughed as he hoisted his sails into a blustery wind.

1. What does the passage tell you about the boy? _____

_____

After dinner the sailor played the concertina. He sang a song about a man named Samuel Blue, who, long ago, tried to sail his boat over land and crashed:

"For the wind o'er land's ne'er
steady nor true,
an' all men that sail there'll
meet Samuel Blue."

2. Why do you think the sailor sings this song to the boy? _____

_____

3. Does the boy listen to what the sailor says in the song? Explain your answer.

_____

4. Why does the boy decide to fly over his village? _____

_____

Determine the Theme

5. What conclusion can you draw about the boy's nature? _____

6. What do you think is the theme of "The Wreck of the *Zephyr*"? What lesson does the

   tale teach? _____

   _____

Macmillan/McGraw-Hill

LINKS IN THE CHAIN OF EVENTS

Information in a story can be organized by cause and effect. That is, one event can lead to another event. Sometimes one cause can have more than one effect. Read each event from "The Wreck of the *Zephyr*" below. Then tell what happens as a result of that event.

Cause: The boy who is a great sailor, takes his boat out on a very stormy day. A gust of wind catches the sail, and the boom swings around and hits the boy in the head.

1. **Effect:** _____

2. **Effect:** _____

Cause: The boy climbs a hill on the island and sees two boats sailing above the water.

3. **Effect:** _____

4. **Effect:** _____

_____

Cause: The boy is determined to make his boat fly.

5. **Effect:** _____

_____

6. **Effect:** _____

_____

Cause: The boy succeeds in making the *Zephyr* fly.

7. **Effect:** _____

8. **Effect:** _____

Cause: The *Zephyr* crashes to the ground.

9. **Effect:** _____

10. **Effect:** _____

11. **Effect:** _____

12. **Effect:** _____

_____

Macmillan/McGraw-Hill

12 | Level 11/Unit 1
ORGANIZE INFORMATION:
Cause and Effect

Extension: Have students write a summary of the story based on the causes and effects they have listed.

5

THE AUTHOR'S ATTITUDE

An author may write to entertain, to inform, and/or to persuade. Also, an author's point of view, or attitude, may or may not be the same as the point of view of the characters in a story. Think about "The Wreck of the *Zephyr*." Answer each question below.

1. Do you think Chris Van Allsburg mainly wrote "The Wreck of the *Zephyr*" to entertain,

   to inform, or to persuade? _____

   The wind whistled in the rigging as the *Zephyr* pounded her way through the water. The sky grew black and the waves rose up like mountains. The boy struggled to keep his boat from going over. Suddenly a gust of wind caught the sail. The boom swung around and hit the boy's head. He fell to the cockpit floor and did not move.

2. How does the passage above entertain the reader?_____

   _____

3. "The Wreck of the *Zephyr*" tells a story within a story. That is, the narrator tells the

   reader a story that was told to him. Why do you think Chris Van Allsburg chose to use

   a story-within-a-story form?_____

   _____

4. Who is the narrator of the story? _____

5. What does the narrator think about the story of the boy who flew his boat?

   _____

6. Do you think the author shares the narrator's point of view about the story of the boy?

   Explain your answer._____

7. In "The Wreck of the *Zephyr*," the old man tells the story to the traveler. What do you

   think the old man thinks about the story of the boy?_____

   _____

8. Do you think the author shares the old man's point of view about the boy's story?

   Explain your answer._____

6 Extension: Have students discuss what they enjoyed most about the story.

Level 11/Unit 1
Author's Purpose and Point of View

Macmillan/McGraw-Hill

SAILING THROUGH THE STORY

Match each sentence beginning with the ending that will form a true statement about the characters in "The Wreck of the *Zephyr*." Write the letter of the answer on the line.

_____ **1.** The narrator

_____ **2.** The boy

_____ **3.** When the sailor on the island

_____ **4.** The old man

a. took the tiller, the boat magically began to lift out of the water.

b. told a story about the *Zephyr* and how it ended up on some cliffs high above the sea.

c. wanted to prove to the villagers and to the sea itself how great a sailor he was.

d. took a walk one day after lunch and came upon an unusual sight—the wreck of a small sailboat on the edge of some cliffs.

Write a paragraph summarizing "The Wreck of the *Zephyr*" on the lines below.

Summary of "The Wreck of the *Zephyr*"

_____

_____

_____

_____

_____

_____

_____

_____

_____

_____

_____

LOOK IT UP!

As you read "The Wreck of the *Zephyr*," you may have come across some unfamiliar words. When you can't use the words around an unfamiliar word to figure out its meaning, you should look up the word in a dictionary. Use the dictionary page below to answer each of the following questions about the word *boom,* which appears in the story.

book•mo•bile \ bŭk′mə bēl′\ *n* : a truck with shelves of books that is a traveling library
¹boom \ büm \ *n* **1** : a long pole used especially to stretch the bottom of a sail **2** : a long beam sticking out from the mast of a derrick or a crane from which the object to be moved is suspended

² boom *vi* **1** : to make a deep hollow rumbling sound ⟨the cannon boomed⟩ **2** : to increase or grow rapidly ⟨business boomed during the war⟩
³ boom *n* **1** : a booming sound **2** : a rapid increase in activity or popularity
boo•mer•ang \ bü′mə rang′\ *n* : a flat curved stick that can be thrown so as to return to the thrower

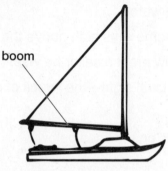

boom

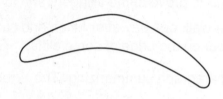

1. How many entries are there in the dictionary for the word *boom?* _____

2. How many definitions are listed in each entry for *boom*? _____

3. Which definition contains the meaning of the word as it is used in the selection?

_____

4. How do you know? _____

5. Which word is just above the first entry for *boom?* _____

6. Which word is just below the last entry for *boom?* _____

7. Which definition of *boom* is used in this sentence: We could hear the boom of the

waves as they pounded on the rocks. _____

8. Which definition of *boom* is used in this sentence: *The sound of the crash boomed*

throughout the village. _____

9. What part of speech is *boom* in the sentence in question 8? _____

10. What part of speech is *boom* as it is used in the selection? _____

Extension: Have students look up the word *tiller* and create a list of questions about this dictionary entry. Then have them exchange lists and answer each other's questions.

Level 11/Unit 1
Reference Sources: Dictionary
10

WORDS IN CONTEXT

Select the correct word from the choices in parentheses.

1. David showed that he was feeling _____ by frowning. (pleased, contrary)

2. When he _____, the class had to wait for him to catch up. (dawdled, raced)

3. Having to dig a _____ of wood out of his finger didn't help, either. (sliver, log)

4. This nature hike through the _____ seemed to be a waste of time. (mall, backwoods)

5. "I'd give _____ to anyone who would take me home right now," David grumbled. (rubies, apples)

6. He sighed and kept _____ his way along the trail. (bouncing, groping)

PAINTING WITH WORDS

Figurative language creates colorful word pictures by comparing two unlike things. Writers use figurative language to help readers understand the meaning of something or help them see something in a new way. Context clues often help you understand figurative language.

Read each sentence below from "The Talking Eggs." Then write the meaning of the underlined word or phrase.

1. They lived on a farm so poor, it looked like the tail end of bad luck.

_____

2. Blanche was sweet and kind and sharp as forty crickets. _____

3. There was even a handsome carriage that grew in a wink from the size of a matchbox—and a fine brown-and-white pony that sprouted from the size of a cricket to

draw it. _____

4. Blanche loaded all these lovely things into the carriage and rode the rest of the way

home like a grand lady. _____

5. So the next morning Rose set out drag-foot into the woods. She dawdled mostly, but

soon met the old woman in her raggedy black shawl. _____

6. But when they got near the cabin and Rose saw the two-headed cow that brayed like a mule and the funny-looking chickens that sang like mockingbirds, she yelled,

"If there ever was a sight, that's one!" _____

7. But out of the shells came clouds of whip snakes, toads, frogs, yellow jackets, and a

big, old, gray wolf. _____

8. These began to chase after her like pigs after a pumpkin. _____

Extension: Have students make up their own figurative expressions to describe Blanche's experiences.

Macmillan/McGraw-Hill

Just Like Sisters

How would you describe Blanche and Rose in "The Talking Eggs"? To make good predictions as you read, you need to be a shrewd judge of character. Write three adjectives to describe each of the two sisters. Then write a sentence describing something each sister did that reveals one of her traits. Then answer the questions.

Blanche's Traits

1. _____ 2. _____ 3. _____

What She Did

4. _____

Rose's Traits

5. _____ 6. _____ 7. _____

What She Did

8. _____

Predictions

9. Based on the traits you saw in Blanche, were you surprised by how she treated the old woman? Why or why not?_____

_____

10. Based on the traits you saw in Rose, were you surprised by how she treated her own sister? Why or why not? _____

_____

11. Would you have predicted that Blanche would take only the plain eggs? Why or why not? _____

12. Would you have predicted that Rose would take only the jeweled eggs? Why or why not? _____

KNOW YOUR CHARACTERS!

The **plot** of a story is the series of events that happen. Characters strongly affect plots. Usually, the more interesting the characters are, the more interesting the plot is.
Think about the characters of Blanche and Rose in "The Talking Eggs." List three character traits for each in the chart below. Then, next to each trait, describe what plot event happened as a result.

CHARACTER TRAITS	RELATED PLOT EVENT

BLANCHE

1. _____

_____

2. _____

_____

_____

_____

3. _____

_____

4. _____

_____

_____

5. _____

_____

6. _____

_____

_____

_____

ROSE

7. _____

_____

8. _____

_____

9. _____

_____

10. _____

_____

11. _____

_____

12. _____

_____

Extension: Have students predict what will happen to Blanche and Rose after the end of the story because of their character traits.

Level 11/Unit 1
ANALYZE STORY ELEMENTS:
Character, Plot

12

Macmillan/McGraw-Hill

THE FRUITS OF KINDNESS

Story events are often organized by cause and effect. A **cause** is the reason why something happens. An **effect** is the result, or what happens. "The Talking Eggs" is a story about human qualities such as kindness, laziness, and greed. Complete the cause-effect chart below. Tell what happened as a result of each cause.

---

1. **Cause:** Rose and her mother were very much alike. Instead of working, they liked to sit on the front porch and talk about being rich.

   Effect: Blanche _____.

2. **Cause:** Blanche gave water to a thirsty old woman.

   Effect: The old woman _____

   _____.

3. **Cause:** Blanche took a long time bringing water back to her mother and sister.

   Effect: Her mother and sister _____.

4. **Cause:** Blanche's mother and sister scolded her and hit her.

   Effect: Blanche _____.

5. **Cause:** Blanche told the old woman that she was afraid to go home.

   Effect: The old woman _____.

6. **Cause:** Blanche promised that she wouldn't laugh at anything she saw at the old woman's house.

   Effect: The old woman _____.

7. **Cause:** Blanche ground one grain of rice in the stone mortar.

   Effect: The mortar _____.

8. **Cause:** Blanche milked the cow in the morning.

   Effect: The two-headed cow _____.

Level 11/Unit 1
ORGANIZE INFORMATION:
Cause and Effect

Extension: Have students write a sentence describing the cause for Blanche's grand new life in the city.

13

A SWEEPING STATEMENT

Folk tales often follow predictable patterns. In some ways, "The Talking Eggs" is a typical folk tale. Think about this tale and other folk tales you know. Then complete the generalizations below. A **generalization** is a broad statement about a topic.

1. In most folk tales the characters are either very _____ or very

    _____.

2. In tales that have a girl as a main character, she often has family members who

    _____.

3. When the main character meets a stranger on the road or in the forest, that person

    often turns out to be _____.

4. In folk tales, kindness to strangers is usually _____.

5. Many folk tales feature animals that _____.

6. The good characters in folk tales always end up _____.

7. The bad characters in folk tales always end up _____.

8. Most folk tales are not completely realistic; they have some events or other elements

    that are _____.

14   **Extension:** Have students form a generalization about Rose's experience with the old woman.

Level 11/Unit 1
Form Generalizations   8

LOOKING FOR TALKING EGGS

Complete the following story map for "The Talking Eggs."

  1. Title: _____

Characters:

  2. _____   3. Two character traits: _____

  4. _____   5. Two character traits: _____

  6. _____   7. Two character traits: _____

  8. _____   9. Two character traits: _____

Settings:

10. _____

11. _____

Plot events:

12. **Beginning of the story:** _____

_____

_____

13. **Middle of the story:** _____

_____

_____

_____

_____

_____

14. **End of the story:** _____

_____

Message of Story

15. _____

Macmillan/McGraw-Hill

CRACKING THE EGG

Read the recipe below for making Egg Drop Soup. Then answer each question.

EGG DROP SOUP

Serves: 2–3

Ingredients:

1 egg
2 1/2 cups chicken broth
cornstarch paste (1 tablespoon
cornstarch mixed with 1
tablespoon water)

1 teaspoon finely chopped tops
of green onion
pinch of white pepper
dash of sesame oil

Directions:

1. In a small bowl, beat egg lightly. Set aside.

2. In a medium-sized saucepan, bring the chicken broth to a boil over high heat.

3. Add the cornstarch paste to the broth, stirring until it comes to a boil again. Reduce the heat to medium-low.

4. Hold the small bowl with the beaten egg about 12 to 15 inches above the pan, and slowly pour the egg into the pan while stirring gently in one direction.

5. Remove the pan immediately from the heat after all the egg has been poured.

6. Sprinkle the soup with the green onion, white pepper, and sesame oil.

Note Any leftover egg drop soup can be used as a stock base for hot and sour soup.

---

1. What preparation step is included in the list of ingredients? _____

   _____

2. What part of the green onion is used? _____

3. What is the next step after beating the egg lightly in a small bowl? _____

   _____

4. What special directions are involved in pouring the egg into the broth? _____

   _____

5. What kind of pepper is sprinkled into the soup? _____

6. What can the leftover egg drop soup be used for? _____

   _____

Extension: Have students draw a picture that clearly illustrates the directions of how to pour the egg into the broth.

Macmillan/McGraw-Hill

WORDS IN CONTEXT

Label each sentence *True* or *False.* If a sentence is false, explain why.

1. A bruised ankle bleeds a lot. _____

    _____

2. Having to wait for the train was a real convenience. _____

    _____

3. The stars are not visible on cloudy nights. _____

    _____

4. Polite people try not to offend others. _____

    _____

5. A letter of protest shows that you approve of something. _____

    _____

6. The foredeck is located over the ship's stern. _____

    _____

7. If you are invited, your presence is requested. _____

    _____

8. A good friend's face is only vaguely familiar. _____

    _____

A STORY MAP TO NARNIA

A story map can help you analyze the elements in a story. Those story elements include characters, setting, and plot. The **characters** are the people in the story. They help create the **plot,** or the series of events that happen. The **setting** is the particular time and place in which the story occurs. Complete the story map below.

Title: The Voyage of the *Dawn Treader*

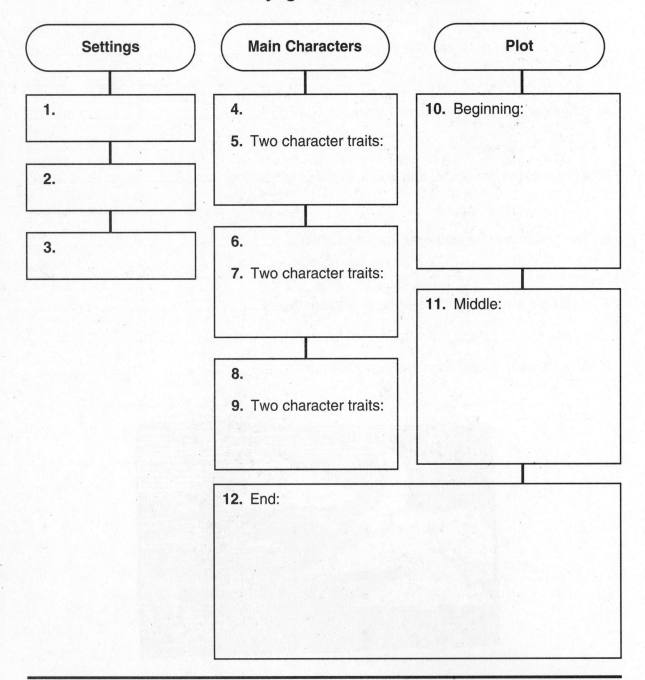

Settings	Main Characters	Plot
1.	4. 5. Two character traits:	10. Beginning:
2.	6. 7. Two character traits:	11. Middle:
3.	8. 9. Two character traits:	
	12. End:	

18   **Extension:** Have students explain why Reepicheep showed his disgust toward Eustace.

Level 11/Unit 1
ANALYZE STORY ELEMENTS:
Character, Setting, Plot
12

Macmillan/McGraw-Hill

WHAT THE EVIDENCE SUGGESTS

An **inference** is a conclusion or deduction made from evidence. Readers make inferences about story elements based on details in the story or their own experience. Review "The Voyage of the *Dawn Treader*," and list traits for each character below. Then answer the questions that follow the character webs.

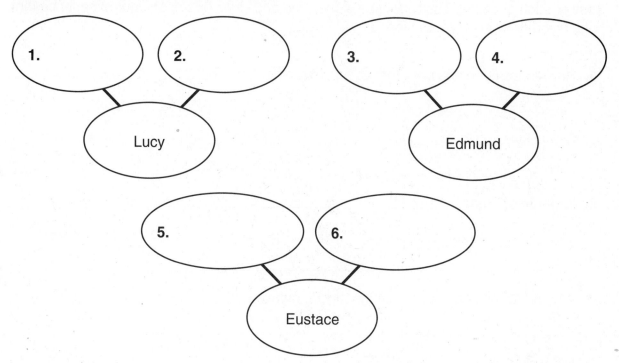

7. What kind of experience do you think Lucy and Edmund have had in Narnia in the past? Give evidence for your answer. _____

_____

8. Do you think that Eustace will have the same kind of experience in Narnia? Give evidence for your answer. _____

_____

9. How do Lucy and Edmund seem to feel about being back in Narnia?

_____

10. What kinds of traits might be most helpful for people visiting Narnia? Explain.

_____

Macmillan/McGraw-Hill

 Level 11/Unit 1
Make Inferences

Extension: Have students fill out a character web for Caspian and then make an inference about what kind of person he is.

19

DRAWING ON WHAT YOU KNOW

Since authors don't always tell readers exactly how the characters in a story feel, it is necessary to draw your own conclusions. To draw a conclusion, you use information based on personal experience and clues provided in a story.

Answer each question. Then describe story clues and clues based on your experience that helped you draw each conclusion.

1. How do Edmund and Lucy feel about each other? _____

_____

2. Story clue: _____

_____

3. Experience clue: _____

_____

_____

4. Why do Edmund and Lucy like the picture of the ship? _____

_____

5. Story clue: _____

_____

6. Experience clue: _____

_____

_____

7. What kind of place is Narnia? _____

_____

8. Story clue: _____

_____

_____

Extension: Have students draw conclusions about the kinds of adventures Edmund, Lucy, Caspian, and Reepicheep have shared in the past.

Level 11/Unit 1
Draw Conclusions

8

Macmillan/McGraw-Hill

FISHING FOR WORD MEANING

Read each passage from "The Voyage of the *Dawn Treader*." Then use context clues to help you figure out the meaning of each underlined word. You may wish to look back at the selection illustrations to help you. Then write each underlined word next to its correct meaning.

• She had only one <u>mast</u> and one large, square sail which was a rich purple.

• Down went the <u>prow</u> of the ship into the wave and up went a great shock of spray. And then up went the wave behind her, and her <u>stern</u> and her <u>deck</u> became visible for the first time.

• There was a lot of shouting going on from the ship, heads crowding together above the <u>bulwarks</u>, ropes being thrown.

• "Come on below and get changed. I'll give you my <u>cabin</u> of course, Lucy, . . ."

• All this she took in in a flash, for Caspian immediately opened a door on the <u>starboard</u> side, and said, "This'll be your room, Lucy."

• "If you'll fling your wet things outside the door I'll get them taken to the <u>galley</u> to be dried."

1. _____ the sides of a ship above the upper decks

2. _____ a pole that holds the sail or sails of a ship

3. _____ a room on a ship for a crew member or passenger

4. _____ a side of a ship, specifically the right side

5. _____ the back part of a ship

6. _____ the kitchen area of a ship

7. _____ the floor on a ship

8. _____ the bow, or front part of a ship

Macmillan/McGraw-Hill

8

Level 11/Unit 1
**CONTEXT CLUES: Content-Area
and Specialized Vocabulary**

Extension: Have students circle any context clues they used to figure out the meaning of each underlined word.

21

PREDICTING AN ADVENTURE

A **prediction** is a guess based on knowledge. Readers make predictions about characters and events in a story based on what the characters are like and what events have already happened.

Think back to when you first read "The Voyage of the *Dawn Treader*." Then answer each question.

1. Were you surprised that the painting pulled the children into Narnia? Explain.

   _____

2. Do you think that Eustace would be scared to be in any situation that was outside of

   his experience? Why or why not? _____

   _____

   _____

3. After only a short time, Lucy felt at home on Caspian's ship. Would you have expected

   that? _____

   _____

4. Do you predict that Eustace will run into trouble with some of the crew of the *Dawn*

   Treader? Explain your answer. _____

   _____

   _____

5. Did anything confirm or cause you to revise your predictions about how Eustace would

   get along with the crew? _____

   _____

   _____

6. What kinds of adventures do you think Lucy and Edmund might have in Narnia this

   time? _____

   _____

22   **Extension:** Have students explain why there might be further trouble between
       Eustace and the valiant, honor-conscious Reepicheep.

Level 11/Unit 1
Make, Confirm, or Revise Predictions

Macmillan/McGraw-Hill

A Voyage Down and Across

Review "The Voyage of the *Dawn Treader*." Then complete the crossword puzzle below.

ACROSS

1. "The Voyage of the *Dawn Treader*" was written by _____.
3. Edmund and Lucy had a secret country called _____.
5. The boy king invited his friends below and gave Lucy his _____.
8. The golden-haired stranger was _____, the boy king.
9. _____ panicked in the water and clutched at Lucy.
10. Lucy and Edmund recognized _____, the Chief Mouse of Narnia.

DOWN

2. The right side of a ship is called _____.
4. Aunt _____ didn't like the picture in Lucy's room.
6. The boy king called Edmund and Lucy their _____.
7. Reepicheep thought Eustace was a singularly _____ person.

10

Level 11/Unit 1
Story Comprehension

Extension: Have students add two more clues to the crossword puzzle.

23

A KNOTTY SET OF DIRECTIONS

Directions help you to make or to do something. Read the following set of directions on how to tie a cat's-paw knot. Then answer each question.

cat's-paw

Directions:

The cat's-paw knot is used to attach a rope to a hook. To tie the knot, first hold one part of the rope in each hand. Then twist the two parts in opposite directions, forming two side-by-side eyes, or holes. Then pass the base of a hook through the two eyes so that a sling hangs from the hook. The cat's-paw knot can be used to lift loads at any angle by varying its position in relation to the sling.

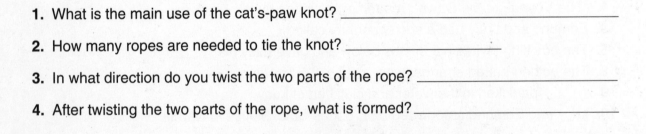

1. What is the main use of the cat's-paw knot? _____

2. How many ropes are needed to tie the knot? _____

3. In what direction do you twist the two parts of the rope? _____

4. After twisting the two parts of the rope, what is formed? _____

   _____

5. What is passed through the eyes of the knot? _____

Macmillan/McGraw-Hill

24   **Extension:** Have students try to make the knot with a piece of rope.

Level 11/Unit 1
Study Skills: Follow Directions
5

WORDS IN CONTEXT

Complete the paragraph with vocabulary words.

flexible	fragile
destruction	management
variety	species
threat	development

Things in nature depend on each other. The balance is often very delicate and

_____. Even the _____ of something small can be a

_____ to the balance. For example, the _____ of a

wilderness camp might seem like a good thing. People could go there to learn about a

_____ of plant and animal _____. But humans

sometimes can be self-centered and not very _____. Meeting visitors'

needs without harming the environment requires careful planning and

_____.

CREATURES GREAT AND SMALL

When you compare and contrast, you pay attention to the ways in which two things are alike and different. In the coral reef, there are many different animals, but even very different animals can be alike in some ways. Use the text and the photographs in "Dive to the Coral Reefs" to compare and contrast the barracuda and the coral. Complete the diagram. Then answer the questions below.

1. Barracuda

_____
_____
_____
_____
_____

2. Both

_____
_____
_____
_____
_____
_____
_____

3. Coral

_____
_____
_____
_____
_____

4. How are a barracuda and coral alike? _____

_____

_____

5. How are a barracuda and coral different? _____

_____

_____

Extension: Ask students to label with a *P* details that they learned about by studying the photographs.

Level 11/Unit 1
ORGANIZE INFORMATION:
Comparison and Contrast

5

Macmillan/McGraw-Hill

POLYPS, PLANKTON, AND PREY

When you read a nonfiction selection, you are likely to come across words that are unfamiliar to you. When this happens, look at the words that surround the unfamiliar word for clues about its meaning.

Read each sentence from "Dive to the Coral Reefs," and use context clues to help you figure out the meaning of the underlined word. You may also go back to the selection and read more of the surrounding context. Then write each underlined word next to its correct definition.

- Each coral animal, or <u>polyp</u>, is about the size of a pencil eraser.

- Like their cousins, the jellyfishes, they use their tentacles to capture their <u>prey</u>: small drifting plants and animals called <u>plankton</u>.

- As they <u>snorkeled</u> over the reef, the divers saw nurse sharks resting on the sand.

- Frightened, the octopus changed colors. These <u>camouflage</u> experts are shy animals, and it is rare to see one in the open.

- Like other plants, *zooxanthellae* use the sun to make food through a process called <u>photosynthesis</u>.

1. _____ dived underwater wearing special breathing equipment

2. _____ hiding by blending in with the background

3. _____ a single coral animal

4. _____ process in which green plants make food using solar energy

5. _____ tiny plants and animals that drift in the ocean

6. _____ animals that are hunted and eaten by other animals

Level 11/Unit 1
**CONTEXT CLUES: Content-Area
and Specialized Vocabulary**
6

Extension: Ask students to circle the word *zooxanthellae* in the list of sentences above. Then have them look for context clues in the selection about the word's meaning.

27

PICTURE PERFECT

"Dive to the Coral Reefs" is a photo-essay. In this type of nonfiction, the photographs both reinforce ideas in the text and provide additional details about the subject. In "Dive to the Coral Reefs," the photos give the reader a "you are there" feeling.

Read each main idea from "Dive to the Coral Reefs" below. Then, using only the photographs, list three details that support the main idea.

Main Idea Divers wear special clothing and equipment when they explore a coral reef.

1. _____

2. _____

3. _____

Main Idea Corals grow in colonies of many different shapes.

4. _____

5. _____

6. _____

Main Idea Many kinds of animals feed or hide in the coral reef.

7. _____

8. _____

9. _____

Main Idea Diving to a coral reef is a fascinating experience.

10. _____

11. _____

12. _____

Extension: Ask students to look at the photographs from the deep reef. Have them list two things they can learn about the deep reef from studying the photographs.

Level 11/Unit 1
ORGANIZE INFORMATION:
Use Illustrations and Photographs

12

A DIFFERENT WORLD

To summarize a nonfiction selection, think about the main ideas presented. Write the main ideas and use each as a topic sentence for one paragraph of your summary. In the rest of the paragraph, present the most important points the author made about the idea.

Complete the paragraphs below to write a summary of "Dive to the Coral Reefs."

1. Although they may not look like it, corals are animals.

_____

_____

_____

2. Corals live close together in colonies that form different shapes.

_____

_____

_____

3. The reef is built by the growing corals.

_____

_____

_____

4. Many creatures find hiding places or food in the coral reef.

_____

_____

_____

5. Coral reefs today face both natural and human threats.

_____

_____

_____

Macmillan/McGraw-Hill

5

Level 11/Unit 1
Summarize

Extension: Ask students to underline in their summaries any new words they learned from reading the selection.

29

GET THE IDEA?

Write an *X* next to *only* the details that support each main idea below.

1. A living coral reef is like an underwater city.

_____ **a.** A coral reef is full of structures.

_____ **b.** Staghorn coral looks like deer antlers.

_____ **c.** Millions of corals live in the reef.

2. Corals are animals, but they are also part plant.

_____ **a.** Corals use tentacles to capture prey.

_____ **b.** Corals have tiny plants growing inside them.

_____ **c.** Corals can be destroyed by anchor-dragging boats.

3. The coral reef provides feeding and hiding places for many sea creatures.

_____ **a.** Coral polyps build new skeletons on top of the old.

_____ **b.** Crabs and worms live in cracks and holes in the reef.

_____ **c.** Nurse sharks eat lobsters and crabs that hide in the reef.

4. Coral reefs grow in tropical oceans all over the world.

_____ **a.** The largest coral reef is the Great Barrier Reef near Australia.

_____ **b.** Special training is needed to make a dive in the deep reef.

_____ **c.** The Pear Tree Reef is in the Caribbean Sea near Jamaica.

5. Coral reefs can be damaged by both natural and human causes.

_____ **a.** Colonies of staghorn coral are often victims of hurricanes.

_____ **b.** Oil spills and ocean dumping can destroy large areas of the reef.

_____ **c.** Some animals in the reef live inside other animals.

6. Different species of coral form colonies of different shapes.

_____ **a.** Plate coral is big and flat like a dinner plate.

_____ **b.** Some parts of the coral reef are more than 5,000 years old.

_____ **c.** Brain coral forms a mound that has many furrows and ridges.

Macmillan/McGraw-Hill

Extension: Have students identify another main idea presented by the authors. Have them write the main idea and two details that support it.

Level 11/Unit 1
ORGANIZE INFORMATION:
Main Idea and Supporting Details   6

JUST THE FACTS?

Most authors of nonfiction write mainly to inform. As they present information, authors often express a point of view, especially when they are writing to persuade. Nonfiction authors may also write to entertain. Read each passage from "Dive to the Coral Reefs." Then answer the questions.

Authors' Point of View (opinion)

It is one of the largest, most colorful, most amazing communities in the world. It is built and inhabited by millions of incredible creatures. It is the living coral reef.

1. How can you tell that the authors think a coral reef is fascinating?

_____

The reef is home to literally millions of plants and animals because it offers good feeding and good places to hide.

2. Do the authors think reefs are important? How can you tell?

_____

Authors' Purpose (reason for writing)

The divers dropped off the reef edge and descended 100 feet down the reef wall. Special training is required to make a dive like this and it challenges even experts!

3. Why do the authors tell readers about the special training needed for deep dives?

_____

_____

Some people are surprised to find out that corals are animals because many look more like plants. There is something amazing about corals that helps to explain their plantlike shapes. Scientists have discovered that coral animals are also part plant.

4. What do you think was the authors' purpose in writing this passage?

_____

Coral reefs can only be preserved through wise ocean management. So maybe someday you, too, can put on scuba tanks and explore this fantastic underwater world.

5. From this concluding statement, what do you think was one of the authors' main

reasons for writing "Dive to the Coral Reefs"? _____

_____

Level 11/Unit 1
Author's Purpose and Point of View

Extension: Ask students to underline words and phrases in the final passage that gave them clues about the author's purpose.

31

THE INCREDIBLE REEF

Think about what you have learned about coral reefs. Then complete the outline below by writing some details about each topic.

The reef as a structure

1. Single coral animals_____

_____

_____

2. How reefs are built_____

_____

_____

3. Shapes of coral _____

_____

The reef as a feeding ground

4. Small creatures _____

_____

5. Large creatures _____

_____

The reef in danger

6. Harm from natural causes _____

7. Harm from human causes _____

_____

8. Protecting the reefs _____

_____

32   **Extension:** Ask students to underline each main topic in the outline.

Level 11/Unit 1
Story Comprehension

8

Macmillan/McGraw-Hill

A HANDY TOOL

Most nonfiction books have an **index**—an alphabetical list of topics—located at the end of the book. Index entries often have subtopics indented underneath. A portion of an index from a book is shown below. Refer to the index to answer each question.

B
baleen whales
   See whales, toothed
blubber, 256
blue whales, 257
C
cetaceans, 252, 264, 265
D
dolphins, 253, 264
dugongs, 256
E
echolocation, 261-262
F
flukes, 254

G
gray whales, 257, 270, 271
M
manatees, 256
marine mammals
   behavior, 264
   communication, 264-265
   migration, 270
   reproduction, 271-273
   swimming/diving, 259
P
pods, 257
polar bears, 253
porpoises, 253

R
right whales, 257
S
sea lions, 251
sea otters, 253
seals, 251
W
walruses, 251
whales
   fossils of, 252-253
   migration of, 260-261
   toothed, 256, 258
   toothless, 256
   types of, 256-259

---

1. On which page(s) are sea otters discussed? _____

2. Which two entries in the index have subentries? _____

3. On which page(s) will you find information about the migration of whales? _____

4. Which page(s) should you read to find out what *echolocation* is? _____

5. Under what entry should you look to find information about baleen whales?

   _____

6. Does this book contain any information about mythical sea creatures? Explain.

   _____

7. On which page(s) would you find how marine mammals swim and dive? _____

8. Under what two entries could you look for information about gray whales?

   _____

UNIT VOCABULARY REVIEW

Underline the words your teacher says.

1. anchor	2. sliver	3. browse	4. dependable
uncle	slicker	bruised	division
anger	silver	breed	development
5. astronaut	6. grating	7. often	8. flecks
astonished	groping	office	friction
atomic	guppy	offend	flexible
9. buttered	10. rabies	11. prescribe	12. Franklin
broader	rubies	preschool	fraction
bordered	ribbon	presence	fragile
13. holster	14. contract	15. convenience	16. threat
hoisted	contrary	competition	throw
hooted	counter	complaining	third
17. treacherous	18. backwoods	19. vaguely	20. variety
treasure	backwards	vacant	very
tremendous	backstep	vacuum	varnish
21. surely	22. visible	23. stone	24. management
shoreline	vegetable	stern	magnify
shearing	visitor	store	maintain
25. doodled	26. apply	27. detection	28. species
dawdled	approve	destruction	speakers
didn't	approach	desertion	seesaws

WORDS IN CONTEXT

Complete the paragraph with vocabulary words.

publicity   discount

organized   dangled

auction   lecture

deliveries   donate

More _____ were coming, and stuff was already piled up

in every corner of the storeroom. Some things even _____

from the ceiling! A few articles in the newspaper and some spots on radio and

TV were all the _____ needed to persuade people to

_____ something to the school's _____.

Nobody had to go around and _____ business owners about

doing the right thing. They just did it! Even stores that never gave students a

_____ were eager to take part in the auction _____

by the students to raise money to help homeless people.

READING BETWEEN THE LINES

Read each passage from "It's Our World, Too!" Answer each question by making an inference from details the author has given. You may wish to look back at the selection for more information.

One day a reporter entered the Lebo garage. Stepping gingerly through the tires and frames that covered the floor, she found a boy with cut fingers and dirty nails, banging a seat onto a frame. His clothes were covered with grease. In her admiring article about a boy who was devoting his summer to helping kids he didn't even know, she said Justin needed bikes and money, and she printed his home phone number.

Overnight, everything changed. "There must have been a hundred calls," Justin says.

1. How would you describe the Lebo garage? _____

2. What details give you a hint that Justin spends a great deal of time in the garage?

_____

3. How did the people who called after reading the reporter's article feel about what

Justin was doing? _____

Her mother's table was covered with a plastic cloth. The plastic gloves from the dime store were laid out. Mountains of ham, turkey, and cheese were at one end.

4. Why are there plastic gloves on the food table? _____

_____

Twenty-three hands went up. When Dwaina excitedly reported this to her mother, Gail Brooks nearly passed out. "Twenty-three kids? Plus *our* family?" "Yeah, Mama, isn't it great! Think how many meals we can make!"

5. Why did Dwaina's mother react this way? _____

_____

"Why don't y'all stay over?" asked Dwaina.
"I'll bring popcorn!" said Claire.
"I got a Hammer tape," said Qiana.

6. Who are Claire and Qiana? _____

_____

Extension: Ask students to underline the details that helped them answer each question.

Macmillan/McGraw-Hill

HUNTING FOR BIKES

Like fictional stories, articles about real people often contain a problem and a solution. Sometimes the person in the article deals with a series of problems. Reread the selection about Justin Lebo. Then complete the chart below.

Problem: Justin was bothered that the two bikes he had fixed were not being ridden.

Solution: 1. _____

_____

Problem: There are 21 boys at the Kilbarchan Home but only 2 bikes.

Solution: 2. _____

_____

Problem: Justin needs a way to build a large number of bikes efficiently.

Solution: 3. _____

_____

_____

Problem: Justin must find and pay for 60 to 80 junker bikes.

Solution: 4. _____

_____

_____

Problem: Justin runs out of money and has less time to work on the bikes.

Solution: 5. _____

_____

_____

_____

Level 11/Unit 2
ORGANIZE INFORMATION:
Problem and Solution

Extension: Ask students what other people, if any, helped in solving the problems listed. Have them circle references to these people in what they wrote above.

37

Macmillan/McGraw-Hill

PLEASE HELP

When writers want to persuade their audience to support a cause, they sometimes use propaganda techniques. In the **bandwagon technique,** the writer tries to make readers feel they should do something because everyone else is doing it. In another technique, the writer uses **loaded words.** These words show the writer's strong feelings (either positive or negative) about the subject.

Read each situation below. Then use the suggested propaganda technique to write your paragraph.

1. Imagine that you are writing a letter to the editor of a newspaper about Justin's project. Write a paragraph that will persuade readers to support it. Use loaded words—such as *saint, unselfish,* and/or *noble*—in your appeal.

Local Boy Builds Bikes for People Who Have None

_____

_____

_____

_____

_____

_____

2. Imagine that you go to Dwaina's school, but you are in a different fifth-grade class. Write a paragraph to persuade your classmates to do a project like Dwaina's. Use the bandwagon technique in your appeal.

Help the Homeless

_____

_____

_____

_____

_____

_____

38 **Extension:** Have students underline the loaded words they used in their answer in the first paragraph they wrote.

Level 11/Unit 2
Persuasion and Propaganda 10

Macmillan/McGraw-Hill

MAKING A DIFFERENCE

A **generalization** is a broad statement based on convincing examples. Justin Lebo and Dwaina Brooks are two examples of young people who have used their skills to help others. Answer each question about Justin and Dwaina. Look back through the selection if you need to. Then use your answers to form a generalization about helping others.

1. Why did Justin begin to fix up old bikes?

_____

_____

2. How does Justin use his skills to make bikes for kids who are orphaned, ill, or homeless?

_____

_____

3. What generalization does Justin make about helping others?

_____

_____

4. When the homeless young man tells Dwaina he would love a really good meal again, why does she feel inspired?

_____

5. What idea does Dwaina get after talking to the young man?

_____

6. How do Dwaina and her classmates make preparing the meals fun?

_____

7. What generalization does Dwaina make about helping others?

_____

8. Based on the examples of Justin and Dwaina, make a generalization about a good way that young people can help others. _____

_____

8 Level 11/Unit 2
Form Generalizations

Extension: Ask students if they think the statements Justin and Dwaina make about helping others (questions 4 and 7) are generally true. Have them explain their answers.

39

How It All Began

Read each list of events from the profiles of Justin Lebo and Dwaina Brooks. Number the events in each list from 1 to 8 to show the order in which they occurred.

Justin

_____ Justin gives the two bikes to boys at the Kilbarchan Home.

_____ Justin fixes up two old bikes for fun.

_____ Justin asks his parents for matching dollars to help him buy old bikes for parts.

_____ Justin begins to run out of bikes and money.

_____ Justin builds bikes for kids in a home for children with AIDS and for others.

_____ Justin decides to make nineteen more bikes for the boys.

_____ A reporter writes an article about Justin's project and asks readers to help.

_____ People donate many bikes and money.

Dwaina

_____ A young homeless man tells Dwaina he would love a really good meal.

_____ Dwaina notices men and women outside a homeless shelter each morning.

_____ Dwaina and her mother carefully shop for food.

_____ Dwaina, her mother, and sisters assemble the meals on Friday nights.

_____ The class sets up an assembly line in the Brooks' kitchen to make more meals.

_____ Dwaina asks her fifth-grade class to help with the meals.

_____ Dwaina asks her mother to help her make meals for the homeless.

_____ Dwaina decides to make many, many more meals.

40

Extension: Have students write a paragraph comparing and contrasting how Justin and Dwaina started their respective projects.

Level 11/Unit 2
ORGANIZE INFORMATION:
Sequence of Events

16

Macmillan/McGraw-Hill

TWO BY TWO

"It's Our World, Too" presents the stories of two young people who take action to make the world a better place. Fill in the chart below to summarize each story.

	Justin	Dwaina
Age	_____	_____
Skills	_____	_____
	_____	_____
	_____	_____
Whom They Helped	_____	_____
	_____	_____
	_____	_____
	_____	_____
What They Did	_____	_____
	_____	_____
	_____	_____
Who Helped Them	_____	_____
	_____	_____
	_____	_____
Advice to Others	_____	_____
	_____	_____
	_____	_____

Extension: Ask students to think of a way in which they could use their own skills or interests to help others. Have them write about what they could do.

WANTED: OLD BIKES

A **classified ad** is a short advertisement placed by someone who wants to sell, buy, or trade something. Classified ads are found in most daily newspapers. Look over the sample classified ads below. Then answer each question.

Food Products	Sporting Goods
Apples and Cider. Closing Nov. 19 for the season. Open daily 9-6. Farmers Orchards, 537-4973.	SuperTrack racing bike. Ultralight aluminum, best hardware, gel seat. Call 694-2701.
Summer Hill Orchard, 1 mile east of Rt. 588 on Glen Rd., 394-9457. We have red delicious, Jonathan, empire, Fuji, and Rome apples. Also fresh sweet cider, apple butter, and gourds. Hours: 10-5, Monday-Saturday.	Used bikes. Many sizes and models. Reasonable prices. Call Jason at 555-2726.
Pets/Pet Supplies	**Wanted to Buy or Trade**
	Wanted: Banjos, guitars, and mandolins. Any condition. Call 394-4857 evenings.
Adorable, fluffy kittens, part Siamese. Call 427-3374.	Wanted to buy: Ping Pong table in good condition. Call 488-3742.
Husky-shepherd mixed puppies, 6 weeks old. Call 393-3095.	
German short-haired pointer. American Kennel Club. Two years old, fully trained. Call 392-4793.	Wanted to trade: International dolls and puppets. My collection is mainly Chinese and Japanese. What do you have? Let's trade! Call Sally at 791-9971.

1. If you are looking for a bicycle, under what heading should you look? _____

2. Suppose you want to find out more about the SuperTrack racing bike. What telephone number should you call? _____

3. When is Summer Hill Orchard open for business? _____

4. What does Summer Hill Orchard sell besides apples? _____

5. How old are the husky-shepherd mixed puppies that are for sale? _____

6. Are the international dolls and puppets for sale? Explain. _____

_____

7. Someone is looking for musical instruments. What kinds? _____

_____

8. Suppose you are looking for a used bike at a reasonable price. How can you tell that Jason might have a good selection? _____

Extension: Have students write three classified ads—one to sell something, one to buy something, and one to trade something.

Level 11/Unit 2
Reference Sources:
Newspapers and Magazines

8

Macmillan/McGraw-Hill

WORDS IN CONTEXT

Complete this paragraph with vocabulary words.

demolished   erected   restore   elegant

contrasting   abandoned   heritage   landscape

The Preservation Society is working to _____ the old

Montgomery Hotel. The Montgomery was _____ in 1850 and

was once the most _____ hotel in this part of the state. Sadly

_____ with the grandeur of its former days, however, the

Montgomery was a single-room-occupancy hotel for many years before closing

altogether in 1985. Since then, the Montgomery has stood empty, crumbling,

and _____—an ugly blot on the _____. It was

nearly _____ three years ago to make room for yet another

parking lot. The Preservation Society rescued the hotel from the wrecking ball

and saved an important part of our city's _____.

MAKE UP YOUR MIND

Think about how New Providence changed over the years. Decide what you liked and disliked in each cityscape. Make your judgments, and then complete the chart.

Year	What I like	What I don't like
1910	1. _____	7. _____
	_____	_____
	_____	_____
1935	2. _____	8. _____
	_____	_____
	_____	_____
1955	3. _____	9. _____
	_____	_____
	_____	_____
1970	4. _____	10. _____
	_____	_____
	_____	_____
1980	5. _____	11. _____
	_____	_____
	_____	_____
1992	6. _____	12. _____
	_____	_____
	_____	_____

Macmillan/McGraw-Hill

44   *Extension:* Have students write a sentence explaining what improvements they would like to see made in their own neighborhood.

Level 11/Unit 2
Make Judgments and Decisions

THE ILLUSTRATED TOWN

Answer each of the following questions about the use of typeface and headings in "New Providence." **Typeface** is the size and shape of the print, words in *bold* (very dark) or *italic* (slanted) typeface often present main ideas or key words in a section. **Headings** are the titles used to introduce new chapters or sections in a work.

1. How are headings used in the selection? _____

2. Why do you think the writers made the typeface in the headings so large and dark?

   _____

3. How would you describe the poetry that introduces the first and last cityscapes?

   _____

4. Why do you think the writers used a different typeface for the poetry?

   _____

Now use the illustrations in the selection to answer the following questions. Circle the letter of the correct answer.

5. Which illustration shows the statue of Chief Tenebo with a sheet over it?

   a. 1910   **b.** 1955   **c.** 1970

6. In the 1955 illustration, what sign has replaced the one for the Butler House?

   a. Rexall   **b.** Pharmacy   **c.** Liquors

7. Which illustration shows a mural saying, "Have a nice day"?

   a. 1910   **b.** 1935   **c.** 1970

8. In the 1935 illustration, what sign sits in the courthouse square?

   a. Coca Cola sign   **b.** WPA sign   **c.** cigarette ad

9. Which of the following two businesses appear in both the 1980 and 1992 illustrations?

   a. Getz & McClure/Butler House   **b.** Getz & McClure/McDonald's

   c. Computer Land/Reiter's Shoes

10. Which illustration shows marchers protesting against the Vietnam War?

    a. 1955   **b.** 1970   **c.** 1980

PERSUASIVE PARTICULARS

The writers of "New Providence" have particular ideas about how a city should be. Positive words and phrases help persuade, or convince, you to like the changes. Negative words and phrases help persuade you to dislike the changes. In the chart below, list some of the positive and negative words and phrases the writers use to describe each cityscape. Some boxes may be blank.

Year	Positive Words and Phrases
1910	1. _____
	_____
1935	2. _____
1955	3. _____
1970	4. _____
1980	5. _____
	_____
1992	6. _____
	_____

Year	Negative Words and Phrases
1910	7. _____
	_____
1935	8. _____
	_____
1955	9. _____
	_____
1970	10. _____
	_____
1980	11. _____
1992	12. _____

Macmillan/McGraw-Hill

46 *Extension:* Have students write three positive phrases to describe their own downtown.

Level 11/Unit 2
Persuasion and Propaganda 12

WORDS TO LEARN BY

Use context clues to help you figure out the meaning of each underlined word below. Then write the meaning of the word.

1. The Colonel Fleming House now <u>accommodates</u> three small businesses within its

   walls. _____

2. The elegant Butler House is now a boarding house for <u>transients</u> and others passing

   through town. _____

3. The building is being covered with <u>prefabricated</u> siding rather than with materials that

   have to be constructed in the square. _____

4. The builders have <u>erected</u> a new skyscraper to house Monarch Insurance.

   _____

5. Safe and quiet, the pedestrian mall was designed to attract <u>suburban</u> shoppers who

   are not used to the city's noise and confusion. _____

6. Once a busy intersection, Main Street has been <u>converted</u> into a pedestrian mall.

   _____

7. The post office has been torn down, and several other buildings have also been

   <u>demolished</u> to make room for a new parking lot. _____

8. Groups of concerned citizens carry paints and brushes to cover up <u>graffiti</u> on the

   downtown walls. _____

9. Many of the old buildings have been <u>renovated</u> so that they look much as they did in

   1910. _____

10. All of the old building <u>facades</u> and many of the back areas have been restored.

    _____

Level 11/Unit 2
**CONTEXT CLUES: Content-Area and
Specialized Vocabulary**

Extension: Have students underline the words and phrases that helped them
figure out each word's meaning.

47

Macmillan/McGraw-Hill

How Do They Compare?

Compare and contrast New Providence in 1910 and 1992, and in 1935 and 1955.
Complete the following charts.

1910 and 1992

Likenesses	Differences
Vendors sell produce on the sidewalk.	1. _____ _____
The bandstand, statue, and circular clock are standing.	2. _____ _____
The Town Hall has a slate roof.	3. _____ _____
The building facades of the Butler House and of Getz & McClure's are similar.	4. _____ _____
The buses in 1992 are made to look like the streetcars of 1910.	5. _____ _____

1935 and 1955

Likenesses	Differences
6. _____ _____	In 1955, the Butler House is a liquor store and boarding house.
7. _____ _____	In 1955, part of the square is paved for car parking.
8. _____ _____	In 1955, buses have replaced the streetcars.
9. _____ _____	In 1955, Getz & McClure's has a new facade and lettering.
10. _____ _____	In 1955, shingles have replaced the slate roof of the Town Hall.

48   *Extension:* Have students add another likeness or difference to each part.

Level 11/Unit 2
ORGANIZE INFORMATION:
Comparison and Contrast

10

A City's Story

Read the following clues about people, places, and things in "New Providence." Write the answer to each clue on the lines below.

1. This is the name of the county New Providence is in and of the man portrayed in the statue. _____

2. These public transportation vehicles were replaced by buses in 1955. _____

3. A sign for this jobs program stood in the courthouse square in 1935. _____

4. This type of highrise began to appear in 1980. _____

5. In 1955, this building burned down. _____

6. The house named for this person was moved to another location in 1980. _____

_____

7. Many of the town's older buildings underwent this process in 1992. _____

8. These advertisements had all been removed by 1992. _____

9. *Lady and the Tramp* played here in 1955. _____

10. In 1992, the city made many changes that were true to this. _____

11. This is the name of the insurance building built in 1980. _____

12. This is the second name on the oldest department store's sign. _____

12

Level 11/Unit 2
Story Comprehension

Extension: Have students write three sentences about their town using any three words in the puzzle.

49

CITY SIZES AND CLIMATES

The buildings, signs, and street furniture shown in "New Providence" can be found in real cities. You can learn about some of these cities by studying the information in the table below. The table contains information about the ten largest cities in the United States in 1990. Use the table to answer each of the following questions.

City	Population	Climate	
		Avg. Temp. in Jan.	**Avg. Temp. in July**
New York City	7,322,564	33° F (1° C)	74° F (23° C)
Los Angeles	3,485,398	55° F (13° C)	73° F (23° C)
Chicago	2,783,726	25° F (-4° C)	75° F (24° C)
Houston	1,630,553	55° F (13° C)	83° F (28° C)
Philadelphia	1,585,577	35° F (2° C)	76° F (24° C)
San Diego	1,110,549	55° F (13° C)	70° F (21° C)
Detroit	1,027,974	26° F (-3° C)	73° F (23° C)
Dallas	1,006,877	46° F (8° C)	85° F (29° C)
Phoenix	983,403	51° F (11° C)	91° F (33° C)
San Antonio	935,933	52° F (11° C)	84° F (29° C)

1. Which city shown on the table has the most people? _____

2. Which city shown on the table has the least people? _____

3. Which cities have more than one million people? _____

   _____

4. Which city has 1,585,577 people? _____

5. Which city has 1,027,974 people? _____

6. Which city has the coldest temperature in January? _____

7. Which city has the coldest temperature in July? _____

8. Which city has the warmest temperature in July? _____

50 *Extension:* Have students write the name of the state where each city listed above can be found.

Level 11/Unit 2
Graphic Aids: Charts and Tables   8

Macmillan/McGraw-Hill

WORDS IN CONTEXT

Label each sentence *True* or *False*. If a sentence is false, explain why.

1. Riding a bike is a <u>stifling</u> experience. _____

_____

2. If you have <u>surveyed</u> a room, you have seen every part of it. _____

_____

3. A hopeful person is in <u>despair</u>. _____

_____

4. A <u>distressed</u> face shows sadness. _____

5. To be <u>speechless</u> is to be at a loss for words. _____

_____

6. <u>Insistent</u> people are always laid-back and relaxed. _____

_____

7. Dried fruits are <u>shriveled</u> and chewy. _____

8. If you are <u>stunned</u> by something, it has no effect on you at all. _____

_____

TWISTS AND TURNS

Character, setting, and plot are closely connected in "The Gold Coin." Juan is a thief who reforms during the course of the story. Doña Josefa is a saintly figure who has a good influence on Juan. Complete the chart below to better understand how the selection's setting, the characters, and the plot all relate to one another.

PEOPLE JUAN MEETS	CROPS JUAN HELPS TO HARVEST	EFFECT OF ENCOUNTER ON JUAN
1. _____ _____ _____ _____	2. _____ _____ _____ _____	3. _____ _____ _____ _____
4. _____ _____ _____ _____ _____ _____	5. _____ _____ _____ _____ _____ _____	6. _____ _____ _____ _____ _____ _____
7. _____ _____ _____ _____ _____ _____	8. _____ _____ _____ _____ _____ _____	9. _____ _____ _____ _____ _____ _____
10. _____ _____ _____ _____ _____ _____	11. _____ _____ _____ _____ _____ _____	12. _____ _____ _____ _____ _____ _____

Extension: Have students identify other elements of character, setting, or plot in this tale. Then ask them to write a paragraph about which element they think is most important.

Level 11/Unit 2
ANALYZE STORY ELEMENTS:
Character, Setting, Plot   12

Macmillan/McGraw-Hill

Coin a Word

Read each passage from "The Gold Coin." Use the context of surrounding words to figure out the meaning of the underlined word. Circle the letter of the correct answer.

1. Juan was half asleep when he heard knocking at the door and the sound of <u>insistent</u> voices. A few minutes later, he saw the woman, wrapped in a black cloak, leave the hut with two men at her side.

    a. weak   **b.** demanding   **c.** quiet

2. The countryside had been <u>deserted</u>, but here, along the riverbank, were two huts.

    a. occupied   **b.** busy   **c.** empty

3. And later that evening, when he helped the young man husk several ears so they could boil them for supper, the yellow <u>kernels</u> glittered like gold coins.

    a. pieces   **b.** ears   **c.** leaves

4. In the <u>stifling</u> heat, the kind that often signals the approach of a storm, Juan simply sighed and mopped his brow.

    a. pleasant   **b.** dry   **c.** airless

5. She was standing by the door, shaking her head slowly as she surveyed the <u>ransacked</u> house.

    a. neat   **b.** messy   **c.** orderly

Level 11/Unit 2
CONTEXT CLUES: Unfamiliar Words

Extension: Have students figure out the meaning of the word *surveyed* in sentence 5. Then have them use the word in a sentence.

53

GUESS WHAT?

Often as you read a story, you make a prediction about what is going to happen. You are able to do this because the author frequently provides clues about the characters and what they are likely to do. Read each passage from "The Gold Coin." Then write what prediction you think most readers would make about what will happen next. You may want to look back at the paragraphs around each passage.

1. Here's my chance! Juan thought. And, forcing open a window, he climbed into the

   empty hut. _____

   _____

2. "Tomorrow," the young man replied softly. "Perhaps I can take you tomorrow, maybe

   the next day. First I must finish harvesting the corn." _____

   _____

   _____

3. Slowly, he pulled out a hand from under his poncho. When his companion grasped it

   firmly in his own, Juan felt suddenly warmed, as if by the rays of the sun. _____

   _____

   _____

   _____

4. Juan's face broke into a smile. It had been a long, long time since Juan had smiled.

   _____

   _____

5. She took the coin out of her pocket and handed it to him. Juan stared at the coin,

   speechless. _____

   _____

6. Juan took in the child's frightened eyes, Doña Josefa's sad, distressed face, and the

   ransacked hut. _____

   _____

54

Extension: Have each student write down a point in the story where they were able to successfully predict what was about to happen next.

Level 11/Unit 2
Make, Confirm, or Revise Predictions

6

Macmillan/McGraw-Hill

ONE FOLLOWS THE OTHER

In the left column are causes for events and situations in "The Gold Coin." In the right column are effects of those causes. Next to each cause, write the letter of its effect.

CAUSE

EFFECT

_____ 1. He steals at night.

a. Juan helps them with their harvest.

_____ 2. Doña Josefa leaves her home.

b. His body is shriveled and bent.

_____ 3. Father and son must finish digging up potatoes before they give Juan a ride.

c. Juan offers to repair her house.

_____ 4. Juan enjoys home-cooked stew and bread.

d. His face is always twisted into a frown.

_____ 5. He hides and sneaks about.

e. Juan enters the empty hut looking for gold.

_____ 6. The girl shows him a family of rabbits.

f. He thinks of other meals.

_____ 7. Doña Josefa can't leave her house with a storm approaching because of the damaged roof.

g. His skin is pale and sickly.

_____ 8. He has no friends or relatives.

h. Juan smiles.

8

Level 11/Unit 2
ORGANIZE INFORMATION:
Cause and Effect

Extension: Have each student write a sentence identifying one other example of cause and effect in this selection.

Macmillan/McGraw-Hill

Go Figure

Sometimes authors tell us how characters feel or why they act a certain way. Sometimes we have to draw conclusions about characters based on information the author has given or information from our own experiences.

Answer each question.

1. What does Juan think when he overhears Doña Josefa say, "I must be the richest person in the world"? _____

   _____

2. How do you think the pleasures of a home-cooked meal and the beauty of a sunset make Juan feel? _____

   _____

3. What seems to happen to Juan as he meets different people along the way in his search for Doña Josefa? _____

   _____

4. What are some of the changes that take place in Juan's appearance during the story, and what do the changes seem to signal? _____

   _____

   _____

   _____

5. What does Juan learn about Doña Josefa during his search for her? _____

   _____

   _____

6. What does Juan's action of returning the gold coin to Doña Josefa tell us about him?

   _____

   _____

   _____

Extension: Have students write a short paragraph in which they draw a conclusion about either Doña Josefa or Juan. In the paragraph, the students should explain why the character feels or acts a certain way, and then provide information from the story or their own experiences that support the conclusion.

56

Level 11/Unit 2
Draw Conclusions

6

Macmillan/McGraw-Hill

PUZZLING QUESTIONS

Use the clues given below to complete the following crossword puzzle.

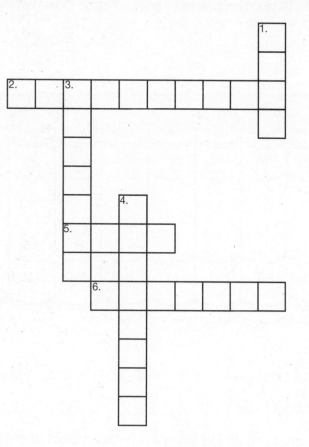

ACROSS

2. the woman who helps everyone and asks nothing for herself

5. that part of her hut which needs repair because of an approaching storm

6. the small animals that make the thief smile when he sees them

DOWN

1. the person who searches for the woman with the gold coin

3. the person to whom the thief wants the woman to give the coin at the end of the story

4. the crop being dug up by the first people the thief meets with

 6 Level 11/Unit 2
Story Comprehension

Extension: Have groups of students make crossword puzzles of their own based on this selection.

57

THE ENCYCLOPEDIA SPEAKS VOLUMES

An **encyclopedia** contains information about many different subjects, which are listed alphabetically. Use the illustration below to answer each question that follows.

Vol. 1	Vol. 2	Vol. 3	Vol. 4	Vol. 5	Vol. 6	Vol. 7	Vol. 8	Vol. 9	Vol. 10	Vol. 11	Vol. 12
A	B-Ci	Ci-D	E-F G-H	I-J K-L	M	N-O	P-Q	R-Se	Sh-Sz	T-U V	W-X Y-Z

1. The author of "The Gold Coin" comes from Cuba. In which volume would you look to find information about Cuba? _____

2. If you were interested in learning more about the subject of coins, in which volume would you look? _____

3. If you were interested in learning more about gold, in which volume would you look?

_____

4. A number of crops are mentioned in "The Gold Coin." What are some of them?

_____

5. In what volumes would you find more information about the crops you listed above?

_____

_____

_____

Extension: Have students make a list of other topics related to this selection that they might like to learn about—for example, horses, ponchos, boats, and so forth. Then have them look up the subject in an encyclopedia in the classroom or in the library and write a paragraph about what they find.

Level 11/Unit 2
Reference Sources: Encyclopedia

Macmillan/McGraw-Hill

WORDS IN CONTEXT

Complete the paragraph with vocabulary words.

typical	collision	avalanche	injured
intense	data	cycle	atmosphere

Predicting weather involves collecting and analyzing many kinds of

_____. Weather forecasters observe changes in the

_____, which is made up of oxygen, nitrogen, and other

gases. By studying _____ weather patterns, they learn what to

expect from each _____ of weather events. For example, they

have to know what happens when a _____ of cold air and

warm air occurs. The pressure to make accurate predictions is

often _____. People can be

_____ or even killed by the weather.

Mountain climbers need to be aware of weather conditions

to avoid being trapped in an

_____.

GENERALLY WHAT HAPPENED

Use what you learned in "The Big Storm" to form generalizations about severe weather and its effects.

What happens when . . .

1. an avalanche roars down a mountain? _____

_____

2. blizzard winds blow? _____

3. a tornado strikes? _____

4. big hailstones fall? _____

5. a cloud lets go of its energy? _____

When snowstorms come to the Midwest and East, what can happen to . . .

6. travelers? _____

7. traffic? _____

8. trains? _____

9. a baseball game? _____

10. school children? _____

60 **Extension:** Ask students to form two more broad generalizations about storms and the effects they have.

Level 11/Unit 2
Form Generalizations 10

GOOD REASONS

In most nonfiction selections, some facts are related as cause and effect. A **cause** is something that makes another thing, the **effect**, happen.

Complete the following chart to tell about cause-and-effect relationships in "The Big Storm."

EFFECT

CAUSE

1. The rainstorm on the Pacific Coast moved inland.

_____

_____

2. Strong winds occur at the leading edge of the storm.

_____

_____

3. _____

The sun heats the atmosphere unevenly.

4. It is not easy to predict what a storm will do.

_____

_____

5. People at the National Meteorological Center are able to forecast many storms.

_____

_____

_____

6. A tornado forms.

_____

_____

7. Static electricity builds up inside a cloud.

_____

8. _____

Arctic air flowed into the Midwest behind the cold front.

8

Level 11/Unit 2
ORGANIZE INFORMATION:
Cause and Effect

Extension: Ask students to circle each cause that they supplied in the chart.

61

WEST WITH THE WIND

When you come across a specialized term in your reading, you can use context clues in both the text and pictures to help determine its meaning. Sometimes, the context may even include a definition of the word.

Read each passage from "The Big Storm" below. Then use context clues in the text and pictures to write a definition of the underlined term.

1. Like most weather systems in North America, it was carried along by the <u>westerlies</u>, the winds that nearly always blow from west to east across the continent.

   _____

   _____

2. The snow began to slide from the high places, gently at first, then faster and faster, until the slides became huge <u>avalanches</u>. The avalanches roared down the mountains and slammed into buildings. _____

   _____

3. Barometers measure the pressure of the air directly overhead. Air, like water, has weight, and tons of air press down on the earth. This force, called barometric or <u>atmospheric pressure</u>, changes constantly as the air moves._____

   _____

4. As the blizzard raged on, the weather stations in the storm reported the low pressure, the freezing temperatures, and the gusty wind and snow conditions to the National <u>Meteorological</u> Center near Washington, D.C._____

   _____

5. Far above the surface, the <u>jet stream</u>, a narrow band of high-speed wind that snakes across the continent, formed a giant curve around the low._____

   _____

   _____

Extension: Ask students to reread passages 1 and 5 and then circle the definition of the underlined word that is given in context.

Level 11/Unit 2
**CONTEXT CLUES: Content-Area and
Specialized Vocabulary**

5

ONE THING LEADS TO ANOTHER

Read each list of sentences. Number the events in the correct order. Look back
at the selection to help you.

1. _____ The wind pushes the clouds up the steep mountains of the Sierra Nevada.

   _____ Ocean clouds bring heavy rain to the Pacific Coast.

   _____ In the cool air, the rain changes to snow.

   _____ Huge amounts of snow begin to slide, causing an avalanche.

   _____ The snow builds up on the mountains.

2. _____ Strong updraft winds produce thunderclouds.

   _____ A wedge of cold, dense air pushes just behind a cold front.

   _____ The cold air forces the warm, moist air to rise very quickly.

   _____ The tornado sucks in air, dirt, and other objects as it travels.

   _____ The updraft winds begin to spin, causing a tornado.

3. _____ A Tornado Warning is broadcast.

   _____ A spotter sights a tornado heading for Paris, Texas.

   _____ Most people survive the tornado.

   _____ The funnel cloud rips through the city.

   _____ Families rush to basement shelters, bathrooms, or closets.

Macmillan/McGraw-Hill

Level 11/Unit 2
ORGANIZE INFORMATION:
Sequence of Events

Extension: Ask students to circle the sequence of events that explains how heat
from the sun makes the atmosphere move.

63

IT'S *SNOW* BIG DEAL

The author of a nonfiction selection includes a great deal of important information that supports her or his main ideas. The author also gives relatively unimportant information to make the selection more interesting and fun to read.

Read each sentence from "The Big Storm." Write *I* next to each sentence that gives important information about the main ideas of the selection. Write *U* if the information is unimportant.

_____ 1. Spring is a time of rapidly changing weather.

_____ 2. Flocks of geese and robins moved north as the days lengthened.

_____ 3. In the cold mountain air the rain changed to snow.

_____ 4. The flakes clung to the tall pines, coating them in heavy layers of white.

_____ 5. Strong cold fronts usually bring high winds and sometimes violent weather.

_____ 6. Heat from the sun causes the atmosphere to flow and swirl around the earth.

_____ 7. Tornadoes are violent whirlwinds, funnel-shaped clouds that may spiral down from thunderstorms.

_____ 8. Dogs whined and hid under beds.

_____ 9. Hailstones form when an ice crystal is coated with freezing cloud mist.

_____ 10. Over a foot of snow fell in New York before the storm moved on to Boston.

64

Extension: Ask students to find another sentence from the selection that contains important information and one that contains unimportant information. Have them write the sentences on a separate sheet of paper.

Level 11/Unit 2
Important and Unimportant Information

10

Macmillan/McGraw-Hill

WEATHER YOU LIKE IT OR NOT

Complete each sentence with information from "The Big Storm."

1. The westerlies are_____

_____.

2. Cold fronts are places where_____

_____.

3. Heat from the sun causes the atmosphere to_____

_____.

4. Barometers measure_____

_____.

5. Weather forecasters use_____

_____.

6. Low-pressure areas are places where_____

_____.

7. Tornadoes form when_____

_____.

8. Raindrops start out as_____

_____.

9. Hail forms when_____

_____.

10. Arctic air moved down_____

_____.

10   Level 11/Unit 2
Story Comprehension   **Extension:** On a separate sheet of paper, have students draw a picture to show
what they learned about one of the topics above.   **65**

ASTOUNDED BY MAPS

A national weather map shows the distribution of temperatures across the nation. Weather symbols for warm and cold fronts, high- and low-pressure areas, and precipitation also appear on the map.

Use the map below to answer the following questions.

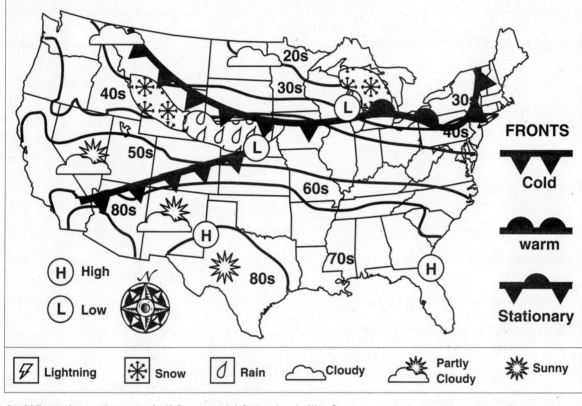

1. What does the symbol for a cold front look like?_____

_____

2. What is the symbol for a high-pressure area (area of high atmospheric pressure)?

_____

3. What temperature is forecast for most of Texas, in the south-central part of the nation?

_____

4. What will the skies look like in that part of the country? _____

5. What will be the coldest temperature in the United States on November 26?

_____

Extension: Ask students to use a map of the United States and the map above to name another state where temperatures in the 80s are forecast.

Level 11/Unit 2
Graphic Aids: Maps

UNIT VOCABULARY REVIEW

Draw a line under the words your teacher says.

1. banded	**2.** demanded	**3.** discourage	**4.** surrounded
abandoned	demolished	discount	survived
bandit	democratic	discover	surveyed
5. elephant	**6.** dangled	**7.** organized	**8.** insect
elegant	danger	organic	insistent
elevator	danced	organist	instrument
9. irrigated	**10.** deliveries	**11.** deserve	**12.** stifling
erected	delicacies	despair	stiffly
dejected	delights	design	stuffing
13. heredity	**14.** domino	**15.** dishonest	**16.** atmosphere
hairdryer	donate	diskette	Atlantic
heritage	donkey	distressed	athletic
17. landscape	**18.** lecture	**19.** scribbled	**20.** cylinder
landmark	ledge	shriveled	cyclone
landslide	licking	shoveled	cycle
21. restore	**22.** action	**23.** special	**24.** date
restyle	auction	spectacles	data
rested	octopus	speechless	dotted
25. contraction	**26.** publication	**27.** struck	**28.** injured
contrasting	publicly	stubby	injustice
controlling	publicity	stunned	inched
29. intend	**30.** avalanche	**31.** collision	**32.** typewriter
intense	available	collection	topical
interest	average	colonial	typical

Macmillan/McGraw-Hill

WORDS IN CONTEXT

Show understanding of the vocabulary words by answering these questions.

1. previous What was the title of the previous selection?

_____

2. congratulated When was the last time someone congratulated you?

_____

3. accurate For what games is accurate aim important?

_____

4. onlookers Who enjoys sports more—the players or the onlookers?

_____

5. division What division is our school in?

_____

6. swollen What could cause an ankle to be swollen?

_____

7. glory Should people play sports for fun or for glory?

_____

8. athletic Which game do you think requires more athletic skill—tennis or golf?

_____

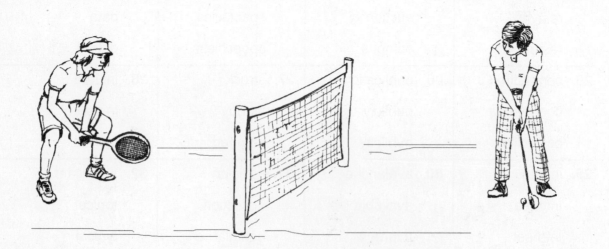

Macmillan/McGraw-Hill

What a Shot!

Plot events and character are often closely linked. By noticing what a character says and does during the events, you can learn what the character is like.

Read each passage below from "The Marble Champ." Then use what you learned about Lupe from the passage to write a word that describes what she is like.

Event	Word That Describes Lupe
1. At the word "marbles," she sat up. "That's it. Maybe I could be good at playing marbles."	_____
2. After school the next day she left her homework in her backpack and practiced three hours straight, taking time only to eat a candy bar for energy.	_____
3. She beat her first opponent easily, and felt sorry for the girl because she didn't have anyone to cheer for her.	_____
4. "I did it!" Lupe said under her breath. She rose from her knees . . . and hugged her father.	_____
5. She thanked her tired thumb. "You did it, thumb. You made me a champion."	_____

BIG PROBLEMS, LITTLE PROBLEMS

In most stories, the main character faces a problem. As the character works to solve the problem, other smaller problems often arise. Complete the chart by describing the solution Lupe found to each problem she faced.

MAIN PROBLEM

1. Problem: Lupe was upset because she was bad at sports.	**Solution:** _____ _____ _____

OTHER PROBLEMS

Preparing for the marbles championship	
2. Problem: At first Lupe's thumb was weak.	**Solution:** _____ _____ _____
3. Problem: Squeezing the eraser made Lupe's thumb sore.	**Solution:** _____ _____ _____

During the marbles championship	
4. Problem: Miss Baseball Cap looked tough to beat.	**Solution:** _____ _____ _____
5. Problem: Dust in Lupe's eyes bothered her.	**Solution:** _____ _____ _____

70   **Extension:** Ask students to draw a line under any references to characters who helped Lupe in solving her problems.

Level 11/Unit 3
ORGANIZE INFORMATION:
Problem and Solution   5

Macmillan/McGraw-Hill

THE THRILL OF VICTORY

Think about what happens in "The Marble Champ." Then complete the story map below.

Setting	1. _____ _____ _____
Main character—traits	2. _____ _____ _____
Other characters	3. _____ _____ _____
Problem	4. _____ _____ _____
Events leading to climax	5. _____ _____ _____ _____
Ending	6. _____ _____ _____

6

Level 11/Unit 3
Story Comprehension

Extension: Ask students to extend the chart by adding the main idea or message of the story.

71

VOLUNTEERS WANTED

When you fill out an application, make sure the information you give is accurate and legible. Read the completed application below. Then answer the questions.

EASTLAKE PUBLIC LIBRARY
Volunteer Application Form (youth)

Name
CUSTER   EMILY   ANNE
Last   First   Middle

Date of Birth
11   22   85
Month   Day   Year

Address
486 WATER STREET   DUBUQUE   IOWA 00000
Number and Street   Town   State and Zip Code

Telephone Number   885 - 7643

Name of Parent(s) or Guardian(s)
MRS. ELLEN CUSTER

Emergency Telephone Number
889 - 8291

Check the events that interest you
☒ Reading to young children   ☐ Making posters
☐ Leading book discussions   ☒ Helping with reading contests
☐ Shelving books

Hours available each week

☐ 1-2 hours   ☒ 2-4 hours   ☐ 4-8 hours

---

1. What is the person who filled out this form hoping to do at the library? _____

   _____

2. What activities are of interest to this person? _____

   _____

3. How much time does the applicant have for volunteering each week? _____

4. How did the applicant show which activities are of interest to her? _____

   _____

5. Why did the applicant write the number *11* above the word *Month* when giving her

   date of birth? _____

72   **Extension:** Ask students to circle the middle name of the applicant.

Level 11/Unit 3
Study Skills: Complete
Forms and Applications

5

Name: _____   Date: _____

WORDS IN CONTEXT

Replace the underlined word or words in each sentence with a vocabulary word.

district	miniature
piers	emerged
regretted	crutch
scheme	monstrous

1. From the top of the mountain, the city looked like a <u>tiny</u> town. _____

2. Everyone screamed when they heard the <u>horrible</u> roar. _____

3. The old house is located in the historic <u>section</u> of the city. _____

4. The two friends <u>felt sorry about</u> the argument, but they both were too stubborn to apologize. _____

5. The injured hiker used a walking stick as a <u>support</u>. _____

6. The water swirled around the steel <u>pillars</u> of the bridge. _____

7. Finally, the plane <u>came into view</u> out of the fog. _____

8. The children devised an elaborate <u>plan</u> to surprise their parents. _____

Macmillan/McGraw-Hill

CLUMSY, BUT CLEVER

Think about how character and setting help to shape the plot of "Breaker's Bridge."
Then answer each question below.

1. Because the river is wide, how does Breaker plan to build the bridge?_____

_____

_____

2. Because the river is powerful and swift, what happens when Breaker and the workers

begin to build the bridge? _____

_____

3. Because Breaker is clever, what task does the emperor give him?_____

_____

_____

4. Because the emperor is cruel, how does he make Breaker's task more dangerous?

_____

_____

5. Because Breaker is kind, what does he do? _____

_____

6. Because of Breaker's kindness, what does the old man do?_____

_____

_____

7. Because Breaker is clumsy, what happens when he tries to use the pellets?_____

_____

_____

8. Because the river becomes strong and wild again every spring, what happens to the

bridge? _____

_____

Extension: Ask students if the story would be as interesting if the emperor were
kind and understanding. Have them explain their answer.

Level 11/Unit 3
ANALYZE STORY ELEMENTS:
Character, Setting, Plot

8

To Bridge or Not to Bridge

Review or reread "Breaker's Bridge." Then add the missing events to the list below.

1. The emperor hears about Breaker's skill as a bridge builder.

↓

_____

_____

↓

2. Breaker's workers begin to build two piers to support the bridge because the river is so wide.

↓

_____

↓

3. Breaker builds a dam to hold back the river while the workers construct stronger piers.

↓

_____

↓

4. Breaker meets a strange old man in the forest.

_____

↓

5. The old man gives Breaker two pellets and tells him to leave one at each spot where he wants a pier.

↓

_____

↓

6. Breaker crushes part of the other pellet as he throws it in the water.

↓

_____

↓

7. Breaker finishes the bridge.

_____

↓

8. In the spring the river destroys the part of the bridge that was not built with magic.

↓

_____

8

Level 11/Unit 3
ORGANIZE INFORMATION:
Sequence of Events

Extension: Ask students to think of an event from the story that is not listed.
Have them add the event to the sequence in its correct place.

75

Macmillan/McGraw-Hill

A Bridge Without Piers?

When you see an unfamiliar word, reading the words and sentences around it can help you figure out what the word means. This is called using context clues.

Use context clues to figure out the meaning of the underlined word in each passage. Then write each underlined word next to its correct meaning below.

Breaker pointed to the two <u>piers</u>. They rose like twin towers toward the top of the gorge. "With a little luck, the emperor will have his bridge."

From the forests of the south came huge logs that were as tough and heavy as iron. From the <u>quarries</u> of the west came large, heavy stones of granite.

And just as he was trimming the last branch from the <u>sapling</u>, he cut the sapling right in two.

The river was too wide to <u>span</u> with a simple bridge. Breaker would have to construct two piers in the middle of the river.

Frightened, Breaker could only stare at the old man. "Ar-ar-are you some mountain spirit?" he <u>stammered</u>.

Breaker leaned over the side and peered below. He could just make out the pale, <u>murky</u> shape of a mound, but that was all.

1. _____ dark and hard to see through

2. _____ a small, young tree

3. _____ towers or tall poles that support a bridge

4. _____ spoke in a confused or nervous way

5. _____ places where building stones are cut out of the earth

6. _____ extend across

76   **Extension:** Ask students to underline the context clues that helped them find the meaning of each word.

Level 11/Unit 3
CONTEXT CLUES: Unfamiliar Words

Macmillan/McGraw-Hill

A RIVER WILD AND STRONG

A **generalization** is a broad statement or rule that is true in many instances. To show that a generalization is valid, or true, you must be able to give several examples to support it.

Below is one generalization that readers can make after reading "Breaker's Bridge." In the chart, list three examples from the selection that support the generalization. Then list three examples from real life that support the generalization.

Generalization: Nature is difficult to tame and change.

Examples from "Breaker's Bridge"	Examples from Real Life
1. _____ _____ _____ _____ _____	4. _____ _____ _____ _____ _____
2. _____ _____ _____ _____ _____	5. _____ _____ _____ _____ _____
3. _____ _____ _____ _____ _____	6. _____ _____ _____ _____ _____

Extension: Ask students to trade pages with a partner and read the partner's examples from real life. Ask them to put a check mark next to each example that supports the generalization.

THINGS CHANGE AND YET DO NOT CHANGE

Review or reread "Breaker's Bridge." Then complete the story map below.

Characters and Traits

Breaker   1. _____

Emperor   2. _____

Old man   3. _____

Setting

Place   4. _____

_____

Time   5. _____

Plot Events

Beginning   6. _____

_____

_____

Middle   7. _____

_____

_____

_____

End   8. _____

_____

_____

Extension: Ask students to add a problem and solution box to the web. Have them identify the main problem Breaker faced and the solution to that problem.

A STRONG AND GRACEFUL BRIDGE

The picture of a modern suspension bridge below is a diagram. In a diagram, an object is drawn in a simplified way and the important parts of the object are labeled.

Answer each question below. Use the diagram.

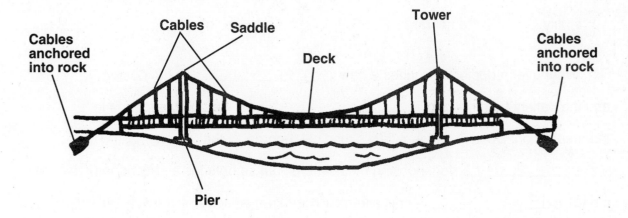

1. What part of the bridge supports it from below? _____

2. How is the bridge supported from above? _____

   _____

3. What is the name for the part of the bridge where the cables run over the top of a

   tower? _____

4. How are the cables anchored to the ground at each end of the bridge? _____

   _____

5. Cables are heavy ropes of twisted steel. What do you think would happen if the ends

   of the cables were not anchored in the ground? _____

   _____

   _____

Level 11/Unit 3
Graphic Aids: Diagrams

Extension: Ask students to look up other types of bridges and make a diagram comparing their different strengths and weaknesses.

79

WORDS IN CONTEXT

Supply the correct words to complete the paragraph.

basis   treatment

technique   reaction

monitor   distinguish

shaky   temporary

Whenever a doctor prescribes a new _____, the doctor

and the patient both need to _____ how the body responds to

the medication. Doctors use a patient's medical records as the

_____ for choosing medications, but sometimes a patient has

a bad _____ or is allergic to certain medicines. A medication

might make someone feel _____ or cause

_____ dizziness. Doctors can help patients

_____ between problems that

require immediate attention and those that can

wait. Every doctor has his or her own

_____ for handling emergency

situations.

Courageous Children

An author might write to: entertain (provide readers with a story to enjoy); inform (give readers information about a topic); persuade (lead readers to think a certain way). Read each passage from "How It Feels to Fight for Your Life." Write *entertain, inform*, or *persuade* to identify the author's main purpose on each line. Then answer each question.

I was seven years old when my mom told me I had diabetes. It was a big shock because other than having to go to the bathroom more than usual I was feeling fine. I had gone to my doctor for a regular checkup and he found sugar in my urine. This was a sign that my pancreas wasn't working right.

1. Author's purpose: _____

2. Why do you think the author chose to use Rachel's voice instead of her own?

_____

_____

There are two kinds of diabetes, Type One and Type Two. In Type One the pancreas can't produce insulin at all. In Type Two there's nothing wrong with the pancreas but the cells in the rest of the body don't respond to the insulin.

3. Author's purpose: _____

4. Why do you think the author included specific details about the two types of diabetes?

_____

The blood test is more annoying than painful—just a tiny little finger prick. The first time I had to have one I was so scared I hid in my father's closet. I sat there behind his shoes and wouldn't come out.

5. Author's purpose: _____

6. How do you think readers feel about Rachel as they read this passage? _____

_____

_____

Macmillan/McGraw-Hill

6

Level 11/Unit 3
Author's Purpose and Point of View

Extension: Have students identify the author's main purpose for writing the selection.

81

Name: _____   Date: _____

THE IMPORTANCE OF IT ALL

Like other nonfiction selections, "How It Feels to Fight for Your Life" contains important and unimportant information. The important information explains what it is like to live with a serious illness. The author includes other information that may be unimportant to her main ideas because it makes the selection more interesting to read. Having the author's main purpose in mind can help you sort out important information from unimportant information.

Read each sentence from the selection. Then write *important* or *unimportant* to describe the information.

1. When my mother explained to me what diabetes was I burst into tears. _____

2. In Type One the pancreas can't produce insulin at all. _____

3. I have Type One, which means that I have to get insulin shots. _____

4. Insulin shots keep the amount of sugar in my blood at the right level but only on a

    temporary basis. _____

5. There's one good thing about not eating sugar, which is that I don't have any cavities!

    _____

6. I like Goldfish a lot because they come in lots of flavors. _____

7. I have to be extremely punctual about my meals and snacks so that the food can

    interact with the insulin properly. _____

8. Besides my regular pediatrician, I see a special doctor for my diabetes every three

    months. _____

9. I made her a paperweight out of rocks and shells, and I crocheted her a little triangle

    that she pinned on her wall. _____

10. Sometimes I wonder if when I grow up anyone will want to marry me because my

    children may have diabetes. _____

82   *Extension:* Have students list five other interesting yet unimportant details
in the selection.

Level 11/Unit 3
Important and Unimportant Information

10

PROVE IT!

A **fact** is a statement that can be proved by reference books, by direct examination, or by an expert. An **opinion** is a statement about how a person feels. An opinion cannot be proved and often includes signal words, such as *I think, I feel,* and *for me.*

Read the following statements from "How It Feels to Fight for Your Life." Then write *Fact* or *Opinion* to describe the statement.

Fact or Opinion?	Statement
1. _____	I felt that my life was going to change completely.
2. _____	There are two kinds of diabetes, Type One and Type Two.
3. _____	I have Type One, which means that I have to get insulin shots.
4. _____	The first time my mother gave me an insulin shot, I could tell she was really scared.
5. _____	Insulin shots keep the amount of sugar in my blood at the right level but only on a temporary basis.
6. _____	My brother, Neil, is great about helping me with my lows.
7. _____	For me, the worst part of having diabetes is not being able to eat whatever I want.
8. _____	I would have to say that I miss maple syrup the most of all the things I'm not allowed to eat.
9. _____	People with diabetes have to eat a certain amount of carbohydrates and more protein than most people.
10. _____	Besides my regular pediatrician, I see a special doctor for my diabetes every three months.
11. _____	I think it would be fun to have a pen pal.
12. _____	My family subscribes to a magazine called *Forecast.*

Level 11/Unit 3
Fact and Opinion

Extension: Have students identify one more fact and one more opinion in the selection.

HOW RACHEL SOLVES PROBLEMS

An author sometimes organizes a nonfiction article according to problems and solutions. In "How It Feels to Fight for Your Life," Rachel's main problem is that she has diabetes. Because of her serious illness, Rachel has other day-to-day problems that she must face and solve.

Complete the problem/solution chart below.

Problems Related to Having Diabetes   **Solutions**

The pancreas doesn't produce insulin. ➡️ 1. _____ _____

Rachel was afraid that the insulin needle would be painful. ➡️ 2. _____ _____ _____ _____

3. _____ _____ _____ ➡️ She eats milk and crackers if the low isn't too bad and drinks orange juice if the low is more serious.

4. _____ _____ _____ ➡️ Rachel wears a Medic Alert necklace that tells people she is an insulin-dependent diabetic. The necklace has phone numbers on it for people to call in case of an emergency.

Rachel has to eat a certain amount of carbohydrates and more protein than most people. ➡️ 5. _____ _____ _____

Extension: Have students describe how Rachel and her family solved the problem of her not being able to eat Halloween candy. Was it a good solution? Why or why not?

Level 11/Unit 3
ORGANIZE INFORMATION:
Problem and Solution

5

Macmillan/McGraw-Hill

LEARNING ABOUT DIABETES

In "How It Feels to Fight for Your Life," you learned many things about diabetes and how a girl lives with the illness every day. Think about what you learned in the selection. Then answer each question below.

1. How old was Rachel DeMaster when she learned that she had diabetes?

_____

2. What was Rachel's first response to learning she had the disease? _____

_____

3. What type of diabetes does Rachel have? _____

4. What is the difference in the two types of diabetes? _____

_____

_____

5. What is the reason that Rachel takes insulin twice a day? _____

_____

6. How does Rachel make sure that her sugar levels are okay? _____

_____

7. When does Rachel experience "lows"? _____

_____

8. What kinds of foods must Rachel and other people with diabetes eat? _____

_____

9. Why is exercise good for Rachel? _____

10. What doctors does Rachel see? _____

_____

11. What effect has Rachel's illness had on her friendships? _____

_____

12. What concerns does Rachel have about the future? _____

_____

Level 11/Unit 3
Story Comprehension

Extension: Have students explain how Rachel's brother supports her.

85

READING BETWEEN THE LINES

Rachel and her mother had to carefully read the labels on food products. The purpose of a food label is to inform consumers, or buyers, of the contents of a product. Read the information on the label below. Then answer each question.

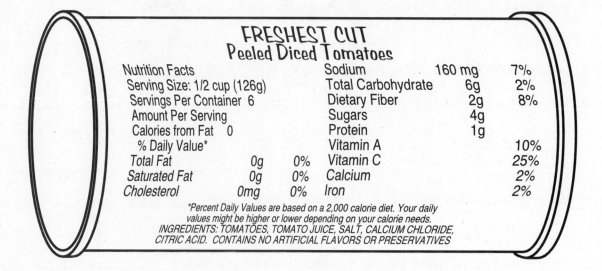

FRESHEST CUT
Peeled Diced Tomatoes

Nutrition Facts			Sodium	160 mg	7%
Serving Size: 1/2 cup (126g)			Total Carbohydrate	6g	2%
Servings Per Container 6			Dietary Fiber	2g	8%
Amount Per Serving			Sugars	4g	
Calories from Fat 0			Protein	1g	
% Daily Value*			Vitamin A		10%
Total Fat	0g	0%	Vitamin C		25%
Saturated Fat	0g	0%	Calcium		2%
Cholesterol	0mg	0%	Iron		2%

*Percent Daily Values are based on a 2,000 calorie diet. Your daily values might be higher or lower depending on your calorie needs.
INGREDIENTS: TOMATOES, TOMATO JUICE, SALT, CALCIUM CHLORIDE, CITRIC ACID. CONTAINS NO ARTIFICIAL FLAVORS OR PRESERVATIVES

1. On what serving size are the nutrition amounts figured? _____

2. What are the percent daily values based on? _____

3. What percentage of total carbohydrate does one serving provide? _____

4. How many grams (g) of dietary fiber are in a serving? _____

5. For which nutritional requirement does a serving provide the second highest

   percentage of daily value? _____

6. What vitamins are provided in each serving? _____

86   *Extension:* Ask students how many calories are provided in one serving.

Level 11/Unit 3
Graphic Aids: Labels

6

WORDS IN CONTEXT

Supply the correct words to complete the paragraph.

sacred	critically
gratitude	intention
captive	starvation

Some people do not approve of keeping animals _____ in

zoos and marine parks. They believe that freedom to live as nature intended is

the _____ right of all living things, and they have spoken out

_____ against keeping wild animals on display. Unfortunately,

the habitats of some species have diminished so much that some animals

would die of _____ if humans did not help them find food.

People sometimes remove animals from their natural environment temporarily

with the _____ of returning them to their own habitat later

on. Anyone who has seen animals that were all but extinct now

thriving at a zoo or a marine park must feel

_____ for the human interference

that made their survival possible.

DETAIL WORK

Writers sometimes organize information in a story according to the main idea and supporting details. A **main idea** is the major, or important, point that a writer makes. **Supporting details** are details that support, or reinforce, the main idea. Read each passage from "Tonweya and the Eagles." Then list the main idea and supporting details.

My father was born in the southern part of what is now Montana. He lived with his people, the Lakota-oyate, or Sioux nation, roaming the Plains of what are now South Dakota, North Dakota, Nebraska, Wyoming, and Montana. My grandfather was named Tasinagi, or Yellow Robe. He was the son of a hereditary chief. He had won his title to chieftainship as a fearless warrior and great hunter. He too was a leader of his people. My grandmother was named Tahcawin, meaning fawn or female deer. My father was her favorite child because he was her firstborn.

1. main idea: _____

_____

2. supporting details: _____

_____

When Chano was about fifteen years old, his dreams of glory in an Indian world vanished. General R. H. Pratt came to the headmen of the tribe and asked them to send one of their children east to a school called Carlisle. He told them that life would change rapidly for them. The buffalo were being killed off and reservations were being formed. He explained that the leaders should know about the new world so different from the Indian way of living.

3. main idea: _____

_____

4. supporting details: _____

_____

The teachers were very kind to him, but until he learned the language and understood them, he did not trust them. He was a good student. He took part in all the athletics and played on the football team. During the summers he worked on the farms. He also attended the Moody Institute summer school at Northfield, Massachusetts.

5. main idea: _____

6. supporting details: _____

_____

Extension: Have students list details supporting the main idea of President Coolidge that Canowicakte was a born leader.

Level 11/Unit 3
ORGANIZE INFORMATION: **Main Idea**
and Supporting Details

6

Macmillan/McGraw-Hill

THE SEARCH FOR MEANING

Many words have multiple meanings. Sometimes you need to figure out which meaning is being used. You can use context clues, or the other words in the sentence or passage, to help you. Read each passage from "Tonweya and the Eagles." Then write the meaning of the underlined word.

1. For a long time he thought his mother had died. He had been the first taken to the barber to have his hair cut. Among the Sioux it is a sign of <u>mourning</u> to do so.

   Meaning: _____

2. Before he left Carlisle, Chauncey Yellow Robe, which was now Canowicakte's name, was chosen to <u>represent</u> the North American Indians at the Congress of Nations at the opening of the World's Columbian Exposition in Chicago.

   Meaning: _____

3. He spoke out many times <u>critically</u>, and in such a way that he was considered a spokesman for the Sioux.

   Meaning: _____

4. Shortly after my father's death, President Coolidge, usually a man of few words, wrote a wonderful <u>tribute</u> to him.

   Meaning: _____

5. He represented a trained and intelligent contact between two different <u>races</u>.

   Meaning: _____

6. He looked at the eagle feather in his father's hair, a sign of bravery, and wondered why it was that the Lakotas as well as many other Indians held Waŋbli, the eagle, in such great <u>respect</u>.

   Meaning: _____

7. He looked below him. There was a <u>sheer</u> drop of many hundreds of feet with not even the slightest projection by which he might climb down.

   Meaning: _____

8. A few berries were growing on the bushes there. He ate them <u>ravenously</u>. Strengthened by even this little food and water, he started off in the direction of the camp.

   Meaning: _____

8

Level 11/Unit 3
CONTEXT CLUES:
Multiple-Meaning Words

Extension: Have students find two other examples in the selection where nearby words help them define a multiple-meaning word.

89

ORDERLY EVENTS

Events in a story happen in a certain sequence, or order. By recognizing that sequence, you can make better sense of a story itself. "Tonweya and the Eagles" has two parts: the foreword and the tale. Within each part, there is a sequence of events. Number each event in each chart in the order in which it happened in the foreword or the tale.

FOREWORD EVENTS

_____ Against Chano's will, he was sent east to a school called Carlisle.

_____ Chano was born in the southern part of what is now Montana, where he lived with his people, the Lakota-oyate.

_____ Chano's hair was cut short, his clothing was taken away, and he was given a uniform to wear.

_____ Canowicakte became known as a "bridge between two cultures."

_____ Canowicakte spent many hours in the tipi of his grandfather and grandmother, learning the legends and history of his nation.

_____ After graduating with honors in 1895, Canowicakte entered government service.

TALE EVENTS

_____ Tonweya climbed the steep cliff with a rope which slipped, leaving him trapped.

_____ When they grew strong, the pair of eagles carried Tonweya from the ledge.

_____ Tonweya went out hunting and shot a buffalo with an arrow.

_____ Tonweya saw an eagle circling, and tried to find the nest.

_____ The two eaglets made friends with Tonweya, who fed them bits of the rawhide rope.

_____ Chano begged his father to tell the story about the sacred birds of Tonweya.

---

90   Extension: Have students add one more event in the proper order to each chart.

Level 11/Unit 3
ORGANIZE INFORMATION:
Sequence of Events   12

Macmillan/McGraw-Hill

PROBLEMS TO SOLVE

Writers often organize information in a story according to problem and solution. In "Tonweya and the Eagles," the main character Tonweya encounters a series of problems, which are solved in surprising ways. Describe the problem or solution in each box below.

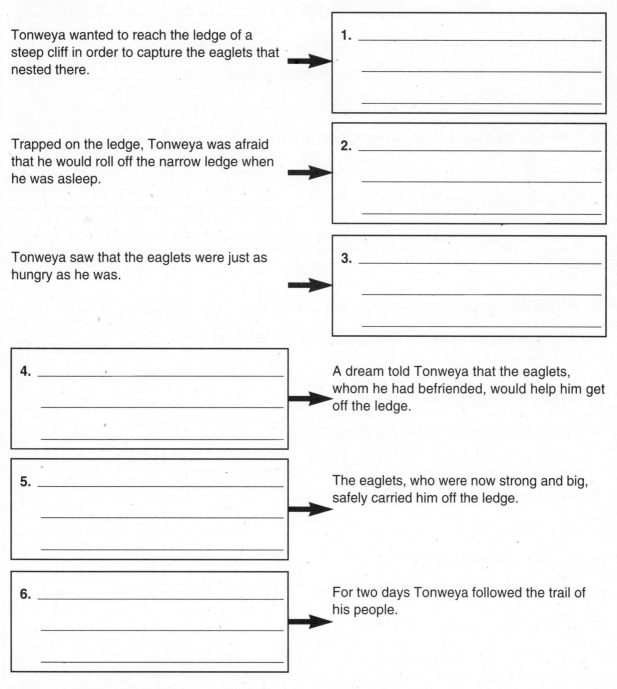

PROBLEM

SOLUTION

Tonweya wanted to reach the ledge of a steep cliff in order to capture the eaglets that nested there.

1. _____
_____
_____

Trapped on the ledge, Tonweya was afraid that he would roll off the narrow ledge when he was asleep.

2. _____
_____
_____

Tonweya saw that the eaglets were just as hungry as he was.

3. _____
_____
_____

4. _____
_____
_____

A dream told Tonweya that the eaglets, whom he had befriended, would help him get off the ledge.

5. _____
_____
_____

The eaglets, who were now strong and big, safely carried him off the ledge.

6. _____
_____
_____

For two days Tonweya followed the trail of his people.

Level 11/Unit 3
ORGANIZE INFORMATION:
Problem and Solution
6

Extension: Have students describe how Tonweya solved the problem of hunger while following the trail of his people.

91

IN THE BEGINNING. . .

Review or reread "Tonweya and the Eagles," and complete the story frame below. Note that the story frame is divided into two parts: the foreword and the tale.

FOREWORD

1. Who is the main character in the foreword? _____

_____

2. Where does the beginning of this true story take place? _____

_____

3. When do the events in the foreword take place? _____

_____

4. What is the purpose of the foreword? _____

_____

TALE

5. Who is the main character in the tale? _____

6. Who is telling the story of Tonweya, and who is listening to it? _____

_____

7. What is the main problem in the tale? _____

8. What happens in the beginning of the tale? _____

_____

9. What happens in the middle of the tale? _____

_____

10. How is the problem solved? _____

11. How does the tale end? _____

12. What is the purpose of the tale? _____

_____

Extension: Have students consider the great change that took place in the life of the author's father. Had they been in his place, would they have preferred to remain on the reservation? Why or why not?

Level 11/Unit 3
Story Comprehension

12

Macmillan/McGraw-Hill

Name: _____   Date: _____

IN THE SHADOWS OF THE ROCKY MOUNTAINS

Look at the map below. Then answer each question.

1. Which state is directly east of Montana? _____

2. What major mountain range passes through Montana, Wyoming, and Colorado?

_____

3. Which three cities in Montana probably have the largest populations?

_____

4. What two states border Wyoming on the east? _____

4 Level 11/Unit 3
Graphic Aids: Maps

Extension: Have students list the names of cities that were probably drawn from
the Native American peoples that live there.

93

Unit Vocabulary Review

Underline the word your teacher says.

1. mentor	**2.** previous	**3.** crush	**4.** distinguish
monitor	precious	crutch	distances
monster	presence	creche	distinct
5. scared	**6.** swell	**7.** pierce	**8.** temper
sack	swollen	price	temporary
sacred	swallow	piers	tarry
9. captive	**10.** cryptically	**11.** starvation	**12.** regular
captivate	critic	salvation	regretted
captain	critically	standardization	regress
13. accrue	**14.** gratitude	**15.** entreat	**16.** skim
accord	grated	treatment	skinny
accurate	attitude	treated	scheme
17. district	**18.** intention	**19.** mirage	**20.** minotaur
distinct	attention	marriage	miniature
discipline	indentation	emerged	mincer
21. athlete	**22.** unhooks	**23.** monstrous	**24.** reaction
athletic	onlookers	monster	reduction
pathetic	lockers	momentous	ration
25. congratulated	**26.** division	**27.** shake	**28.** technique
congregate	derision	shaky	technical
conquer	decision	shaking	tectonic
29. galore	**30.** baskets		
gory	basics		
glory	basis		

WORDS IN CONTEXT

canvas	hovering	smeared	peddler
rascals	bachelor	mustache	blurted

Complete this letter with vocabulary words.

Dear Mom and Dad,

I'm having a great time with Aunt Margaret. I bought some really neat shoes

from a street _____. They are made of _____ like

sneakers. Yesterday, we met a man with a bushy beard and a _____.

He looked as if he'd _____ grease in his hair. The man kept

_____ around Aunt Margaret. Finally, I asked him if he was married

or a _____. I just _____ it out. That made him go

away. Aunt Margaret laughed and told me I was one of the worst

_____ she had ever seen!

I miss you both.

Love,

Jen

JUDGING THEIR DECISIONS

In reading a story, you make judgments about the actions of the characters. That is how you decide whether or not you like a character, or whether the character is believable.

Answer each question below about the characters in "The Best Bad Thing."

1. What bad decision did Rinko make that resulted in the first bad thing? _____

_____

_____

2. What did Auntie Hata say to Rinko about what she did? _____

_____

3. How did Rinko attempt to make up to Auntie Hata for her bad decisions? _____

_____

_____

4. Do you like Rinko more or less for her efforts to make up to Auntie Hata? Why?

_____

_____

5. Whose bad judgment results in the second bad thing? _____

_____

6. What is the second bad thing that happens? _____

_____

7. Who shows good judgment and remains calm after Abu's accident? _____

_____

8. Do you admire Auntie Hata more or less because of the way she handled Abu's

accident? Explain your answer. _____

_____

_____

Extension: Have students identify other examples of judgments or decisions the characters make in this selection, and then have them express their own judgments about the characters.

96

Level 11/Unit 4
Make Judgments and Decisions

8

Macmillan/McGraw-Hill

DRAW AT THE COUNT OF THREE!

Sometimes authors tell us how characters feel or why they act a certain way. At other times, we have to draw conclusions about characters.

Answer each question below by drawing your own conclusions about the character's actions or feelings.

1. What did Rinko think that helping Auntie Hata with the household chores would

   demonstrate? _____

   _____

   _____

2. Why does Rinko feel guilty when Abu is injured? _____

   _____

   _____

3. How did the old man feel about Mr. Sabatini calling him by a nickname? _____

   _____

   _____

4. Would you conclude that Auntie Hata liked Rinko? Explain your answer. _____

   _____

   _____

5. What did Rinko's parents think about her decision to stay with Auntie Hata? _____

   _____

   _____

6. What kind of relationship do Rinko and her parents have? Explain. _____

   _____

   _____

6 | Level 11/Unit 4
Draw Conclusions

Extension: Have students draw a conclusion about the feelings of Rinko toward
Auntie Hata at the beginning of the story.

97

WHO'S TELLING THIS STORY?

Many stories are written in such a way that it seems one of the characters is telling the story. This first-person point of view limits the reader to knowing only what the narrator character knows or experiences. If an author wants the reader to know more, however, the writer will use a third-person point of view. The narrator is outside the action in a third-person point of view. The reader sees things from a wider perspective.

Read the following passage from the selection. Then answer the questions that follow.

> I wished I could get my two more bad things over with fast, but I certainly couldn't break any of Auntie Hata's dishes. She didn't have that many to spare.
> What really made me feel so awful about the whole thing was that Auntie Hata didn't get mad when I told her what I'd done. What she said was, "Ah, well, Rinko, I guess you're still only a child after all."

1. Who is telling the story? How do you know? _____

_____

2. Is this a first-person or third-person point of view? _____

3. What can you tell about Rinko from this passage? _____

_____

Read the following revision of the above passage. Then answer the questions that follow.

> Rinko wished she could get her two other bad things over with fast, but she certainly couldn't break any of Auntie Hata's dishes. She didn't have any to spare.
> Auntie Hata had to smile to herself. Rinko was such a serious girl! When Rinko told her what she had done, Auntie Hata forced herself to put on a straight face and say solemnly, "Ah, well, Rinko, I guess you're still only a child after all."

4. Who is telling the story now? _____

_____

5. Has the story become third-person, or is it still written in the first-person? _____

_____

6. How is this version different? Which point of view do you prefer? Explain.

_____

_____

Extension: Have students write a paragraph from the first-person point of view about their weekend. Then have them write about their weekend from the third-person point of view. Ask them to compare and contrast the two paragraphs.

Level 11/Unit 4
ANALYZE STORY ELEMENTS:
Narrative Point of View

6

BUILD A CHARACTER, BUILD PLOT

In a story, events make a character grow or change. Sometimes what happens to a character is a result of the kind of person he or she is.

Answer the following questions.

1. How did Rinko change over the course of the story? _____
   _____
   _____

2. What is one event that helped change Rinko? _____
   _____
   _____

3. What happened to Abu and Zenny when they ignored Rinko's warning and ran after
   the freight train? _____
   _____
   _____

4. What character traits of Abu and Zenny made them act the way they did? _____
   _____
   _____
   _____

5. What was the old man like? _____
   _____
   _____

6. Was the old man an interesting character? Why or why not? _____
   _____
   _____

6

Level 11/Unit 4
ANALYZE STORY ELEMENTS:
Character, Plot

Extension: Have each student choose a character from his or her favorite
television show, and ask them to write a paragraph about how that character was
influenced by a recent event in the show.

99

PUZZLES ARE FUN/SO LET'S DO ONE!

Use each clue below to review the major characters in the story by filling in the crossword puzzle.

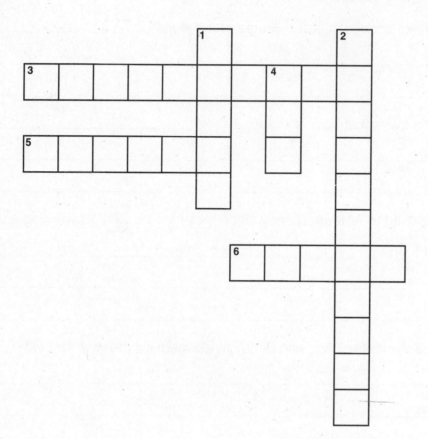

DOWN

1. leads Rinko to the Eagle Cafe after the accident

2. place where Auntie Hata lives

4. has arm mangled by a train

ACROSS

3. recently widowed, has two sons

5. seems unfriendly and mysterious to Rinko

6. sprains her ankle

100   **Extension:** Have students list the story events as if they are train cars. What event would be the engine? What event would be the caboose?

Level 11/Unit 4
Story Comprehension

 6

INFORMATION, PLEASE

Look at this sample listing from a telephone directory. Then answer the
questions below.

178   Barron-Bustamente

Barron William	1099 Center 555-0697	**Bicycle Shop**	**8421 Sullivan 555-1829**
Barwell Harold	956 Bruce 555-3489	Bidderman SR	404 Tredwell 555-8642
Belladona Arturo	3154 Main 555-1432	**Bijou Theater**	**504 Central 555-1990**
Bermudez Sylvia	973 Chestnut 555-2345	**Bob's Big Boy Burgers**	**765 Valley 555-1655**
Best George	217 Duffy 555-5309	Bora JP	345 Mountain 555-8776
Bett's Tire Company	**879 Frontage 555-2145**	Bowman Cissy	247 Collegiate 555-3490
Beveridge Thomas	541 Sheridan 555-4567	Boxerman Albert	5432 Kincaid 555-2314
Bewick HR	654 Dodge 555-1923	Boyer Charles	7089 Rosemary . . .555-9876
Beymouth Richard	321 Sherman 555-4194	Bufone D	341 McCaskey 555-1278
Bezak Trucking	**765 Skokie 555-3211**	Bullock S	312 Sunset 555-0987

1. What number might you call for a snack? _____

2. What is the address of the Bezak Trucking company? _____

3. How many businesses are listed, and how can you tell at a glance?

   _____

4. What is Cissy Bowman's telephone number? _____

5. What is the address of the Bicycle Shop? _____

5

Level 11/Unit 4
Reference Sources: Telephone Directory

Extension: Have students make up their own class telephone book. Include
students' phone numbers, emergency numbers, etc.

101

WORDS IN CONTEXT

Rewrite this paragraph, replacing the underlined words and phrases with vocabulary words.

afford	rejected
permission	burglar
thieves	submitted

It seemed as if things couldn't get much worse for the young, struggling author. A week ago, <u>robbers</u> _____ had stolen his typewriter, and he couldn't <u>spare the money</u> _____ to buy a new one. He couldn't imagine why a <u>person who would break in</u> _____ would even be interested in his old typewriter. Without a typewriter, he feared that the last story he <u>sent in</u> _____ to the magazine might be the last one he would ever write. When he received a letter from the magazine, he was sure they had <u>turned down</u> _____ his story. To his delight, however, the editor was asking for <u>consent</u> _____ to print the story in their August issue!

PROBLEM SOLVED

There are a number of problems and solutions presented in "Dear Mr. Henshaw." For each problem below, circle the letter of the correct solution.

1. Someone keeps stealing things from his lunchbag.

    a. Leigh sets up a video camera.

    b. Leigh rigs up a burglar alarm.

    c. Leigh calls the police.

2. Leigh wants to win the prize for the writing contest, but he still hasn't written anything.

    a. He decides to write a story about traveling with his father in a truck.

    b. He decides it is too late to try so he does not submit anything.

    c. He copies a poem out of a book and says he wrote it.

3. Barry's mother is annoyed that his little sisters keep setting off the room alarm that Barry and Leigh have rigged up.

    a. Barry and Leigh make it into a silent alarm.

    b. His mother forbids Barry's little sisters to keep setting off the alarm.

    c. Barry disconnects the alarm.

4. Leigh is upset that his parents are divorced and wants to find a way to fix things between them.

    a. He suggests that his parents get married again.

    b. He tries to find a new girlfriend for his father.

    c. He tried to find a new boyfriend for his mother who will be a good stepfather to him.

5. Feeling shy and awkward, Leigh wants to think of something interesting to say to Mrs. Badger, the "Famous Author."

    a. He is too embarrassed to talk to her and leaves the room.

    b. He ignores her and talks to his schoolmates.

    c. Mrs. Badger starts a conversation by asking him questions about his story.

Macmillan/McGraw-Hill

5 Level 11/Unit 4
ORGANIZE INFORMATION:
Problem and Solution

Extension: For each day in Leigh's diary, have students list a problem that Leigh describes.

103

BETWEEN THE LINES

When we read, we usually make inferences about characters and events. Making inferences means reading between the lines to figure out such things as what a character is feeling or intends to do.

Answer the following questions to clarify what Leigh or other characters are feeling at different points in the story.

1. How does Leigh feel about Barry coming to his house for supper?_____

_____

_____

2. Referring to Barry, Leigh writes in his diary, "It helps to have a friend." What does this statement suggest about the way Leigh is feeling?_____

_____

_____

3. What things about Barry's life might Leigh wish that he had?_____

_____

_____

4. Why do you think Leigh gets angry when his mother says, "Your father isn't a bad man by any means"?_____

_____

_____

5. What do you think Miss Neely thinks about Leigh's abilities as a writer?_____

_____

_____

_____

Extension: Have students write a paragraph about Leigh's relationship with his father, making inferences about the relationship. Encourage them to support their inferences with evidence from the text.

Level 11/Unit 4
Make Inferences

5

DEAR DIARY

"Dear Mr. Henshaw" is told in Leigh's words in the form of diary entries. In other words, you read about what is happening from Leigh's point of view. His entries tell you a lot about what Leigh thinks and feels. For each event from "Dear Mr. Henshaw" listed below, write a detail that Leigh includes and write what Leigh feels or thinks about that event.

Young Writers' Contest

1. Detail from Leigh's Diary: _____

_____

2. What Leigh Feels or Thinks About the Event: _____

_____

_____

Riding on the Rig with His Dad

3. Detail from Leigh's Diary: _____

_____

_____

4. What Leigh Feels or Thinks About the Event: _____

_____

_____

Meeting the Famous Author

5. Detail from Leigh's Diary: _____

_____

6. What Leigh Feels or Thinks About the Event: _____

_____

_____

6

Level 11/Unit 4
ANALYZE STORY ELEMENTS:
Narrative Point of View

Extension: Have students imagine they are either Mrs. Badger, Barry, Leigh's mom, or Leigh's dad. Have them describe an event in "Dear Mr. Henshaw" from their character's point of view.

105

DAY BY DAY

Write a brief summary of Leigh's diary entry for each date below.

1. March 20 _____

_____

_____

_____

_____

2. March 24 _____

_____

_____

_____

3. March 25 _____

_____

_____

_____

_____

_____

_____

4. March 26 _____

_____

_____

_____

5. March 30 _____

_____

_____

_____

_____

106   **Extension:** Have students write a short narrative of their week's events in diary form.

Level 11/Unit 4
Story Comprehension   5

BECOMING FAMILIAR WITH E-MAIL

The illustration below shows what your computer screen might look like if you were sending e-mail. Use the illustration to answer each question.

```
┌────────────────────────────────────────────────────────────┐
│ ■         ▓▓▓▓▓▓▓▓▓▓▓  Untitled 1  ▓▓▓▓▓▓▓▓▓▓▓            ⊡ │
├────────────────────────────────────────────────────────────┤
│                 To:    ┌──────────────────────────┐  ⬆      │
│    ◆Send               │ rickmorales@compPR.com   │         │
│                        │                          │  ⬇      │
│                        └──────────────────────────┘         │
│             Subject:  ┌───────────────────────────┐         │
│                       │    "Dear Mr. Henshaw"     │         │
│    📓                  └───────────────────────────┘         │
│  Addresses    ┌────────────────────────────────────┐ ⬆      │
│               │ Rick,                              │        │
│               │ I just read this great story called│        │
│               │ "Dear Mr. Henshaw."                │        │
│               │ It's about a boy who writes to his │        │
│    📎          │ favorite author                    │        │
│  Attach File  │ (whose name is Boyd Henshaw). The  │        │
│               │ neat thing is Mr. Henshaw writes   │        │
│               │ back!                              │        │
│               │ It gave me a great idea. Why don't │        │
│               │ you and I e-mail our favorite      │        │
│               │ authors, and see if they reply?    │        │
│               │ What author would you e-mail?      │        │
│               │                                    │        │
│               │ What do you think?                 │        │
│               └────────────────────────────────────┘ ⬇      │
│                                                         ⊡   │
└────────────────────────────────────────────────────────────┘
```

1. What brief e-mail message would you like to send to the author of the above

   message?_____

   _____

2. Where would you type his or her e-mail address?_____

   _____

3. What's the subject of your e-mail message? Write your answer here._____

   _____

4. On which icon would you click if you wanted to send a photograph of yourself along

   with your e-mail message? _____

5. On which icon would you click to send your message? _____

⬛
5

Level 11/Unit 4
Reference Sources: Technology   Extension: Have students discuss their experiences sending and receiving e-mail. **107**

Macmillan/McGraw-Hill

WORDS IN CONTEXT

Label each sentence *True* or *False*. If a sentence is false, explain why.

1. Authorities know a little about everything.

   _____

2. When you tell who did a good thing, you are giving credit.

   _____

3. A document must be handwritten.

   _____

4. A patriot is someone who runs for public office.

   _____

5. Historians study and sometimes write about the past.

   _____

6. If you are giving up, you are attempting something.

   _____

7. If a plan is well thought out, it's reasonable to think it will work.

   _____

8. People who do good work can be proud of their achievements.

   _____

Macmillan/McGraw-Hill

MANY MEANINGS

You can use context clues to figure out the meaning of words that have more than one meaning. Read each sentence below. Then circle the letter next to the correct meaning of each underlined word.

1. The <u>leaves</u> of the manuscript were numbered from 1 to 100.

   a. pages   **b.** part of a tree

2. He needed a magnifying glass to read the mouse's <u>minute</u> handwriting.

   a. period of time   **b.** very small

3. Benjamin Franklin had a great <u>fund</u> of knowledge. He seemed to know something about everything.

   a. supply   **b.** an amount of money

4. The mouse first saw Franklin as he tried to write by the dim <u>light</u> of a candle.

   a. not heavy   **b.** brightness

5. Every time Ben Franklin sneezed, his <u>glasses</u> flew off his head.

   a. device to help people see   **b.** drinking cups

6. When Franklin got excited about his work, he would <u>fly</u> from one part of the house to the other.

   a. to move fast   **b.** insect

7. The big piece of black <u>pipe</u> carried the smoke from the stove to the chimney.

   a. a hollow tube   **b.** device used by smokers

8. When Amos had to explain very simple things to Ben, he thought that Ben was a bit <u>dull</u>.

   a. not sharp   **b.** stupid

9. He used a screwdriver to fasten the <u>nuts</u> on the stove.

   a. food with a hard shell   **b.** small pieces of metal

10. Amos had to scold Ben sometimes and be <u>sharp</u> with him when Ben got excited.

   a. not dull   **b.** harsh in tone

10

Level 11/Unit 4
CONTEXT CLUES:
Multiple-Meaning Words   Extension: Have students write a sentence using each word's other meaning.   **109**

DECIDE FOR YOURSELF

Before you make a decision about something, you must first consider the reasons for and against your choice. Read each situation below. List two reasons for each choice, and then write your final decision.

1.–5. Suppose you were Amos and you lived in the church with your large family. Would you look for a new place to live or would you remain at home?

Two reasons for leaving home:

_____

_____

Two reasons for not leaving home:

_____

_____

Final decision:

_____

6.–10. Suppose you were Ben Franklin and you just saw Amos jump into your cap. What would you do with the mouse? Would you let Amos spend the night in your cap or chase him back out into the street?

Two reasons for letting Amos spend the night:

_____

_____

Two reasons for chasing Amos back into the street:

_____

_____

Final decision:

_____

Extension: Have students list the reasons why they should and should not study for a test. Then ask them to make a judgment about what they should do and write their final decision.

Level 11/Unit 4
Make Judgments and Decisions

Macmillan/McGraw-Hill

TRUE OR FALSE?

"Ben and Me" contains many **facts**, or statements that can be proved to be true. It also contains many **nonfacts**, or statements that can be proved to be false. Read each statement below. Write *F* if it is a fact. Write *N* if it is a nonfact. Then write two more facts and nonfacts.

_____ **1.** Benjamin Franklin had a great fund of knowledge.

_____ **2.** Franklin was a great man and a patriot.

_____ **3.** Franklin lived in Philadelphia during the time of the story.

_____ **4.** Franklin wore square-rimmed glasses.

_____ **5.** Franklin was a scientist, inventor, printer, editor, author, soldier, statesman, philosopher.

_____ **6.** "Ben and Me" was written by a mouse who was Franklin's closest friend and adviser.

_____ **7.** Amos the mouse and the members of his family could talk and think.

_____ **8.** Amos gave Franklin the idea for the Franklin stove and helped him build it.

_____ **9.** Ship-rats told Amos how the sailors built their cooking fires on board ship.

_____ **10.** Amos was in great part responsible for Franklin's success and fame.

11.–12. Two More Facts: _____

_____

_____

_____

13.–14. Two More Nonfacts: _____

_____

_____

_____

LOOK WHO'S TALKING

"Ben and Me" is told from the point of view of Amos, one of the story's characters. When you read the selection, you are reading about people and events the way Amos sees them. In the chart below, list five things Amos tells you about himself and five things he tells you about Ben. Then answer each question following the chart.

What Amos Says About Himself

1. _____
   _____
   _____

2. _____
   _____
   _____

3. _____
   _____
   _____

4. _____
   _____

5. _____
   _____
   _____

What Amos Says About Ben

6. _____
   _____
   _____

7. _____
   _____
   _____

8. _____
   _____
   _____

9. _____
   _____

10. _____
    _____
    _____

11. Who does the narrator consider to be more intelligent—himself or Ben? Why?

    _____

12. Do you think your opinion of Ben would be different if the story were told from Ben's

    point of view? Why? _____

    _____

Level 11/Unit 4
ANALYZE STORY ELEMENTS: **Narrative**
Point of View, Setting, Plot

12

112   **Extension:** Have students choose a scene from the selection, and rewrite it from Ben's point of view.

Macmillan/McGraw-Hill

A Mouse's Tale

Below is a list of important events from "Ben and Me." Number each event from 1 through 8 to show the order in which the events happened.

_____ 1. Ben gets the idea for placing the stove on a layer of sand and bricks.

_____ 2. Amos tells Ben that his family used to gather around a chestnut for warmth.

_____ 3. Amos tells Ben how sailors build their cooking fires on board ship.

_____ 4. Amos leaves his family to make his own way in the world.

_____ 5. Ben attaches a smoke pipe to the stove.

_____ 6. Amos enters a house and recognizes Benjamin Franklin.

_____ 7. Ben gets the idea for the Franklin stove.

_____ 8. Amos climbs into Ben's fur cap to sleep for the night.

Next to each sentence beginning in the left column, write the letter of the correct ending in the right column.

_____ 9. Officials from the National Museum of Natural History stated that

_____ 10. Amos asked Ben if he would be going through the pantry because

_____ 11. The first time Amos saw Ben,

_____ 12. Scientists at the Brownsonian Institute

_____ 13. After the stove had been completed, Ben said,

_____ 14. When Amos told Ben how to raise the stove off the floor, Ben said,

_____ 15. Robert Lawson, who wrote the story's foreword,

a. presents Amos's story in the mouse's own words.

b. analyzed the manuscript's paper and ink.

c. the manuscript had been written by a mouse.

d. Ben was trying to write by the light of a candle.

e. "Amos, you've got it!"

f. "Amos, we've done it!"

g. Amos wanted something to eat.

15 Level 11/Unit 4
Story Comprehension

Extension: Have students write a summary of the selection using the list of events above.

113

FACTS AT YOUR FINGERTIPS

Almanacs are published every year and contain information on a wide variety of subjects. The excerpt below is from an outline of United States history that appears in an almanac. Read the excerpt. Then answer each of the following questions.

1712

Slaves revolted in New York, April 6. Six committed suicide and 21 were executed. In the second uprising in 1741, 13 slaves were hanged, 13 burned, and 71 deported.

1716

The first theater in colonies opened in Williamsburg, Va.

1732

Benjamin Franklin published first *Poor Richard's Almanac*. It was published annually to 1757.

1735

Freedom of the press recognized in New York by acquittal of John Peter Zenger, editor of *Weekly Journal*, on charge of libeling British Gov. Cosby.

1740-41

Captain Vitus Bering, a Dane employed by Russians, reached Alaska.

1744

King George's War pitted British and colonials against the French. Colonials captured Louisburg, Cape Breton Is., June 17, 1745. It was returned to France in 1748 by Treaty of Aix-la-Chapelle.

1752

Benjamin Franklin, flying kite in a thunderstorm, proved lightning is electricity, June 15. He invented the lightning rod.

1. Which years in American history are covered by the excerpt? _____

2. What happened in 1716? _____

3. What began in 1744? _____

4. What was the name of Benjamin Franklin's almanac? _____

5. Between what years did Franklin publish his almanac? _____

6. What happened in 1712 and then again in 1741? _____

7. When was freedom of the press first recognized? _____

8. On what exact date did Franklin prove lightning is electricity? _____

Macmillan/McGraw-Hill

Extension: Have students add a paragraph to the almanac entry above. Ask them to write about something that happened in the United States during the current year.

114

Level 11/Unit 4
Reference Sources: Almanac   **8**

WORDS IN CONTEXT

Answer these questions that use the vocabulary words.

1. entertains   What do you think entertains young children the best?

_____

2. carnival   What might you see during a carnival parade in New Orleans?

_____

3. jutted   If you were standing on a rock that jutted out over the ocean, how would you feel?

_____

4. expression   What kinds of things can the expression on your face reveal about you?

_____

5. originate   Where did stories about Coyote the Trickster originate?

_____

6. overhung   Why might a tree branch that overhung a street have to be cut down?

_____

Macmillan/McGraw-Hill

BY THE SEA

You can learn about the characters in "A Wave in Her Pocket" by thinking about their actions and words. The chart below lists some of the things that the characters do and say. Write what each comment or action reveals about the character's personality.

Character's Comment or Action	What It Reveals About . . .
"We knew Tantie would pick the car *she* wanted to ride in."	1. Tantie: _____ _____
The children try to cheer up Tantie.	2. The children: _____ _____
Tantie smiles when she sees the trees, hills, and countryside.	3. Tantie: _____ _____
Amber puts her head on Tantie's shoulder and squeezes her hand.	4. Amber: _____ _____
Every day Delphine feeds the turtles so they will learn to trust her.	5. Delphine: _____ _____
Delphine wants to tell Godfrey not to go to sea but can't.	6. Delphine: _____ _____

Think about when and where the events in "A Wave in Her Pocket" take place and the mood that is set. Then answer each of the following questions.

7. Why is Tantie so quiet in the car on the way to Toco?_____

_____

8. Why does a tear roll down Tantie's cheek when she sees the sea from the car

window? _____

9. How does Tantie feel when Amber explains the meaning of the song to her?

_____

10. Will Tantie still be reluctant to come to Toco in the future?

_____

Extension: Have students use the chart above to write a sentence describing Amber's personality.

10

Macmillan/McGraw-Hill

FANCIFUL PHRASES

Figurative language is a phrase that can't be understood when defined word for word. Writers use figurative language to express ideas in an imaginative way. Each passage below from "A Wave in Her Pocket" contains at least one example of figurative language. Underline each figurative language phrase. Then write its meaning.

1. The sun had just started lighting up the tops of the coconut trees. They looked like giant candles. _____

2. When everyone was ready, we drove off down the narrow pitch road, one behind the other like a trail of goats. _____

3. The sea sprang up all around. It was sparkling like a blue Carnival costume.

   _____

4. The waves were smacking the rocks with big kisses and then ducking back into the sea. _____

5. Even the rocks looked different here. They jutted out from the land like big, brown fishermen waiting to catch fish. _____

6. I was sitting on the other side of the turtle. He was so big it looked like Tantie and I were at a table for two. _____

   _____

7. She had brown skin like de rocks, long braids like de seaweed, and everyone said her eyes were like de midnight wave. _____

   _____

8. Delphine watched Godfrey set out in his pirogue. But this time she felt a darkness deep down inside herself. _____

9. She looked in his eyes and saw de sea. And his smile was better than de sun.

   _____

10. Every day she climbed de rock and looked at de sea for Godfrey. But only de waves looked back at her. _____

WHAT DO YOU INFER?

When you make an inference about a character or event in a story, you make a judgment based on what you have read. Read each statement about "A Wave in Her Pocket." Then circle the letter of the best inference.

1. The narrator explained that tanties always have a story ready for the children.

   a. The children go to someone else when they want to hear a story.
   b. The children look forward to seeing their tantie.
   c. Tanties aren't good storytellers.
   d. Tanties are shy around the children.

2. When the huge turtle saw Amber and her family, he stuck his head back in his shell and sat on the beach like a rock.

   a. The turtle was glad to see them.
   b. Amber was afraid of the turtle.
   c. The turtle was frightened.
   d. The turtle died.

3. Tantie told Amber that the name of the girl in the story was Delphine. Amber remembered that Delphine was also Tantie's name.

   a. The story is about Amber.
   b. Amber has heard the story before.
   c. The story is about a turtle.
   d. The story is about Tantie.

4. Tantie loved Godfrey, but she was too shy to talk to him. Still, one day she stepped up to him and touched his hand.

   a. She wanted to tell him something.
   b. She wanted to see his eyes.
   c. She thought he was ugly.
   d. She wanted to hold his hand.

5. When Godfrey didn't return from the sea, Delphine thought she heard the waves singing a song to her.

   a. Godfrey sang the song.
   b. The song was for Delphine.
   c. Amber sang the song.
   d. The song was for Amber.

6. When Amber told Tantie that she thought she knew what the song meant, Tantie had a far-away look in her eyes.

   a. Tantie was thinking about turtles.
   b. Tantie was thinking about lunch.
   c. Tantie was thinking about another story.
   d. Tantie was thinking about Godfrey.

118 **Extension:** Have students underline the context clues in each statement that helped them make an inference.

Level 11/Unit 4
Make Inferences

6

Macmillan/McGraw-Hill

IN A NUTSHELL

Read each of the following passages from "A Wave in Her Pocket." Then write a one-sentence summary.

1. We could barely see each other over the big basket. I hoped Tantie would open it up and share out some black cake or plums. But Tantie sat there like she was at the movies, her two eyes staring straight ahead, as Daddy drove down the street.

    _____

2. She looked out Susan's window and smiled at the trees and the sky. She looked out the front window and smiled at the next hill coming up. Then she looked out my window where the blue sea was shining in the sunlight, and her smile disappeared clean off her face.

    _____

3. She climbed on top a tall, smooth rock that overhung de rocks where de turtles hid and she dropped small fish below. Then she waited on her rock and watched as turtle heads popped out to snap up de fish. Each day de girl took them fish to eat and after a while de grandfather turtles began waiting for her.

    _____

4. As de girl grew older she began to love something even more than her grandfather turtles. Actually, it was someone. His name was Godfrey and he was a young fisherman. Every morning de girl stood on de beach and watched Godfrey set out in his little pirogue. And every afternoon she waited for him to pull in his nets.

    _____

5. De next afternoon Delphine climbed on top her rock again. She waited and waited. She even forgot to feed de turtles. But Godfrey still didn't come. Every day she climbed de rock and looked at de sea for Godfrey. But only de waves looked back at her.

    _____

6. Marrying someone means that person will always be right next to you, and carrying something in your pocket means de same thing. So, when de song said to marry your love and carry him in your pocket, it meant to keep Godfrey close to you always. Like in your heart, I guess.

    _____

Level 11/Unit 4
Summarize

Extension: Have students summarize what happens after Amber explains the song to Tantie.

119

A Song of the Sea

Below are some statements about the characters and events in "A Wave in Her Pocket." Write *T* on the line if the statement is true. Write *F* it is false.

_____ 1. In Trinidad, a tantie is usually a grandaunt who entertains the children on outings by taking them fishing.

_____ 2. Amber's father decided to take his family to Toco because it's the best beach in Trinidad for a sea bath.

_____ 3. Amber and her brother and sister tried to get Tantie to talk during the car trip to Toco.

_____ 4. The trees, sky, and pretty hills around Toco just seemed to make Tantie feel sadder.

_____ 5. A huge turtle walking on the sand at Toco stuck his head in his shell when he saw Amber and her family coming.

_____ 6. While some of Amber's family looked for a good place to picnic, Tantie told Amber a story.

_____ 7. Delphine never loved anything or anyone more than her grandfather turtles.

_____ 8. Amber guessed that the story was about Tantie when she was a young girl.

_____ 9. Godfrey returned from the sea but decided to move far away to a town in West Africa.

_____ 10. Amber said that the song was from Godfrey telling Delphine to never forget him.

Match each character or word in the first column with the correct description in the second column. Write the letter of the description on the line.

_____ 11. Delphine   **a.** She tried to cheer up Tantie.

_____ 12. pirogue   **b.** His eyes were like the sea, and his smile was like the sun.

_____ 13. Godfrey   **c.** She explained the meaning of the song to Tantie.

_____ 14. Susan   **d.** Godfrey set out to sea in one of these to catch fish.

_____ 15. Tantie   **e.** She had long braids like seaweed and eyes like the midnight wave.

_____ 16. Amber

    f. She told a story about a girl who loved the sea.

120   **Extension:** Have students write a sentence explaining why the song the waves sang to Delphine was a happy song.

Level 11/Unit 4
Story Comprehension

16

Macmillan/McGraw-Hill

MAP IT OUT FOR ME

At the beginning of "A Wave in Her Pocket," the author says that many of the stories that tanties tell originate in the countries of West Africa. Ghana is a country in western Africa. Look at the map of Ghana below. Then use the map to answer each of the following questions.

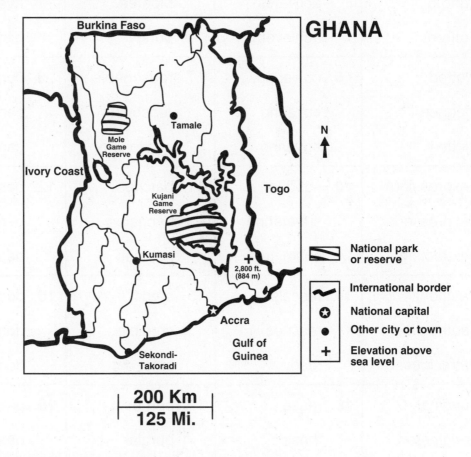

1. What is the national capital of Ghana? _____

2. What country is west of Ghana? _____

3. What country is east of Ghana? _____

4. What country is north of Ghana? _____

5. What are the two game reserves in Ghana? _____

6. What gulf borders Ghana?? _____

7. What is the approximate distance in miles and kilometers between Sekondi-Takoradi

   and Accra? _____

Level 11/Unit 4
Graphic Aids: Maps

Extension: Have students check another map of Ghana and find the rivers. Then have them label five rivers in Ghana on this map.

121

UNIT VOCABULARY REVIEW

Underline the words your teacher says.

1. effort	2. actual	3. blurted	4. historians
afford	activates	bloated	hysteria
affront	achievements	burst	historic

5. jotted	6. cowering	7. reasonable	8. compass
jogged	covering	reasoning	campus
jutted	hovering	seasoning	canvas

9. expression	10. subdue	11. batches	12. permission
expressed	submarine	bachelor	permitted
extracting	submitted	botches	permanent

13. authorize	14. rascals	15. credit	16. dockyard
authorities	rescues	credible	doctorate
atrocious	raspy	crescent	document

17. original	18. tease	19. burger	20. patriot
originate	these	burglar	patrol
errands	thieves	butler	partridge

21. caramel	22. rejected	23. smeared	24. overhung
carnival	regretted	sneered	overhand
carnivore	regimen	sneaked	overhead

25. peddler	26. mustard	27. intertwines	28. attention
puddles	mustang	entrances	attending
meddles	mustache	entertains	attempting

Macmillan/McGraw-Hill

Name: _____   Date: _____

WORDS IN CONTEXT

Label each sentence *True* or *False.* If a sentence is false, explain why.

1. Taking a picture is a way of <u>capturing</u> a happy moment. _____

_____

2. If you use a cake mix, you are making a cake from <u>scratch</u>. _____

_____

3. If you can't sit still, you are <u>restless</u>. _____

_____

4. If you are comfortable in new situations, you are <u>bashful</u>. _____

_____

5. If your great-grandmother had paying guests stay in her house and take their meals

there, she <u>boarded</u> people. _____

_____

6. A period of usually frequent and heavy rain is called a <u>drought</u>. _____

_____

6

ESSIE'S JOURNEY

In "Grandma Essie's Covered Wagon," Essie's family moved from Missouri to Kansas and Oklahoma and then back to Missouri. Understanding what Essie liked about the places, people, and experiences can help you make inferences about her. To make an inference, use details from the story and what you already know from your own experiences.

Read each passage from the selection. Then answer each question.

> Kenneth rode up front with Papa. Jack and I rode wherever we felt like. Sometimes when we were restless, we'd even jump out and trot behind the wagon. We'd throw dirt clods at each other or ride Molly. There were lots of wild things outside—wolves, coyotes, foxes—but if they scared us, we'd just jump back inside and be safe.

1. What did Essie enjoy about the wagon ride to Kansas? _____

_____

> Most of the land was prairie. It rolled on forever, like the back of some huge animal that might get up and run. The wind would whip out of nowhere, and sometimes Jack and I would grab the thick cushions off the sofa, take them outside, and hold them against our bellies. When the wind blew, we'd let go. The cushions would hold to us like magic!

2. What did Essie like about the Kansas prairie? _____

_____

> Papa lost all his money, and we had to sell the farm. I said good-bye to my ducks. Our hound dogs, Papa gave to some neighbors. We auctioned off our horses, cows, and furniture, keeping only what would fit into the wagon, then we loaded it up and were gone. Stella played "Diamonds in the Rough" as we bumped down the dusty road.

3. How do you think Essie felt about leaving? _____

> Grandma'd tell us animal stories every night, smoking a clay pipe that we loved to light. . . . There was a big garden behind their cabin, and a kitchen that wasn't fastened on, and always plenty to eat. We camped at their place all summer and never wanted to leave.

4. What did Essie like about living with her grandparents? _____

_____

5. What can you infer about the kind of person Essie was? _____

_____

6. Why do you think Essie never moved again from Missouri? _____

_____

_____

124

Extension: Have students make inferences about what was most important to Essie about the covered wagon.

Level 11/Unit 5
Make Inferences

6

Macmillan/McGraw-Hill

WHY?

A **cause** is the reason why something happened. An **effect** is the result of a cause, or what happened. Look over "Grandma Essie's Covered Wagon" and complete the chart below by writing in the missing cause or effect.

CAUSE	EFFECT
Essie's father dreamed of a better life than working as a hired hand in Missouri.	1. _____ _____ _____
2. _____ _____ _____	Essie and her brothers and sisters went barefoot through summer and fall and even walked barefoot to school.
A drought came to Kansas.	3. _____ _____ _____
4. _____ _____ _____	Essie's Papa had to sell their farm.
In Big Heart, Stella played her mandolin and sang in the streets all winter to help raise money for the orphanage.	5. _____ _____ _____
6. _____ _____ _____	Essie and her family picked and boxed the ripe strawberries, and then shipped them out on the train.

Macmillan/McGraw-Hill

Level 11/Unit 5
ORGANIZE INFORMATION:
Cause and Effect

6

Extension: Have students explain what caused Essie's Papa to break up the old covered wagon and make furniture from its pieces.

IN CONCLUSION

When you draw a conclusion, you use facts from a story as well as your own knowledge and experience to make a decision. Drawing conclusions as you read can help you better understand a story. Answer each question below.

1. What kind of relationship did Essie and her brothers and sisters have?_____
   _____
   _____

2. What facts from the selection helped you draw that conclusion? _____
   _____
   _____

3. What conclusion can you draw about Essie's Papa based on his decision to go west
   and farm wheat?_____
   _____

4. What facts from the selection helped you draw that conclusion? _____
   _____
   _____
   _____

5. What conclusion can you draw about Papa's feelings toward his daughter Stella?
   _____

6. What facts from the selection helped you draw that conclusion?_____
   _____
   _____

7. What conclusion can you draw about the effect of the drought on people's lives?_____
   _____

8. What facts from the story helped you draw that conclusion? _____
   _____

Extension: Ask students what conclusion can be drawn about Essie based on her
willingness to help the family out by waiting tables.

Level 11/Unit 5
Draw Conclusions

8

Macmillan/McGraw-Hill

STARTING IN MISSOURI

In a story, events are organized usually by sequence, or the order in which the events happen. Recognizing the sequence of events can help you better understand what happened in the story. In "Grandma Essie's Covered Wagon," events happened as the family traveled from Missouri to Kansas, Oklahoma, and back again to Missouri.

Read each passage from "Grandma Essie's Covered Wagon" below. Next to each event, write a number from 1 to 12 to show the order in which the events occurred.

_____ 1. Jack and I loved standing in the stairwell and yelling our names. We'd try to see who could be the loudest, our voices echoing back.

_____ 2. We headed south, down to Oklahoma. Mama's folks lived near Oologah in a log cabin that reminded us of our home in Missouri.

_____ 3. I was born in a log cabin near Duenweg, Missouri, almost ninety years ago.

_____ 4. At first he thought I was seeing things, but then he hollered, "It's a tornado!" and rushed us all to the cellar.

_____ 5. Papa set a tent up in a shantytown where other oil workers' families lived, and we parked the covered wagon. We sold our mules. Papa, Kenneth, and Arthur got jobs in the oil fields and were gone sunup to sundown, and always came home exhausted.

_____ 6. Papa bought a frame wagon that farmers had used to haul crops. He bent wooden stays from one side to the other, nailed them down to form hoops, and stretched a white canvas over.

_____ 7. After a year in Big Heart we had saved enough to go. We bought two new mules and loaded the covered wagon for the last time.

_____ 8. Papa raised wheat, hay, and corn, but the second year in Kansas came a drought.

_____ 9. One cold day in March, Stella died.

_____ 10. Mama thought I could get a job waiting tables, to help the family out.

_____ 11. Then Christmas day, Opal had her baby! We tiptoed upstairs to peek at our first nephew, as big as a hand, healthy and screaming.

_____ 12. Somehow, a front-row girl and I became friends. She had red hair and could really jump rope. She wore beautiful shiny black shoes, but I got to where I barely noticed them.

Macmillan/McGraw-Hill

Level 11/Unit 5
ORGANIZE INFORMATION:
Sequence of Events

Extension: Have students explain what events happened after the family moved back home to Missouri.

Essie's Summary

Imagine that you are young Essie. Write a letter that she might have written to her grandparents in Oklahoma, after she returned to Missouri. Include six important events from the selection so that your letter becomes a summary of "Grandma Essie's Covered Wagon."

Dear Grandma and Grandpa,

    I am writing to tell you that we have finally returned to Missouri. We live near Seneca, which is on the border between Missouri and Oklahoma. Many things have happened to us since we first left Missouri.

1. _____
_____
_____

2. _____
_____
_____

3. _____
_____
_____

4. _____
_____
_____

5. _____
_____
_____

6. _____
_____

Your loving granddaughter,

Essie

Extension: Have students write a summary explaining what was special to Essie about staying with her grandparents in Oklahoma.

Level 11/Unit 5
Summarize

6

Macmillan/McGraw-Hill

ON THE ROAD WITH ESSIE

Think about the characters and events in "Grandma Essie's Covered Wagon."
Then complete the chart below.

Setting	1. _____ _____
Main Characters	2. _____ _____
Point of View Selection Is Told From	3. _____ _____
Beginning	4. _____ _____ _____
Middle	5. _____ _____ _____ _____ _____
End	6. _____ _____ _____

6 Level 11/Unit 5
Story Comprehension

Extension: Have students explain what they found most memorable about this selection.

129

Number of Farms

A **graph** is a special diagram used to organize and present numerical information. A bar graph, like the one below, shows amounts. In a bar graph, the larger the bar, the greater the amount.

Review the bar graph below. It shows the number of farms in Kansas, Missouri, and Oklahoma in the years 1980 and 1989. Then answer each question.

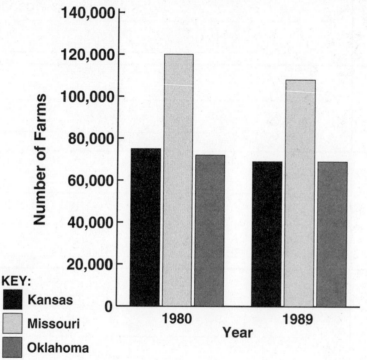

Number of Farms in Kansas, Missouri, and Oklahoma

KEY:
- Kansas
- Missouri
- Oklahoma

1. What do the numbers along the side show? _____

2. What do the numbers along the bottom show? _____

3. Which of the three states had the largest number of farms in 1980? _____

4. Approximately how many farms did Kansas have in 1980? _____

5. Which two states had about the same number of farms in 1989?

_____

6. Did the number of farms in Missouri increase or decrease from 1980 to 1989?

_____

130   **Extension:** Have students use information on the bar graph to describe the trend in number of farms.

Level 11/Unit 5
Graphic Aids: Graphs

6

WORDS IN CONTEXT

Complete this advertisement with vocabulary words.

millionaire	poverty
assembled	guaranteed
advantage	prospector

WANTED: PEOPLE OF VISION

If working hard to avoid _____ is not your idea of a good life, you may be

the person we are looking for. If you want the _____ of being your own

boss and working only when you want to, we have the answer you've been looking for. We

have _____ a book of "get rich quick" ideas that are

_____ to make you a _____. If you have a pan, you too

can be a successful gold _____. Order your copy of this amazing book

now for only $1,000!

WHAT HAPPENED WHEN?

Events in a story happen in a certain sequence, or order. Recognizing that sequence helps readers make sense of the story.

Beside each event from "Klondike Fever," write the correct date from the list below.

1894	July 15, 1897
1896	July 17, 1897
Summer 1897	Winter 1897

_____ 1. A new ship left for the Klondike almost every day.

_____ 2. George Washington Carmack, Tagish Charley, and Skookum Jim discovered gold on Bonanza Creek.

_____ 3. The steamer ship *Excelsior,* the first of the gold ships, arrived in San Francisco.

_____ 4. The Canadian government passed a law forbidding gold miners to enter the fields without enough supplies to last one year.

_____ 5. The *Portland* arrived in Seattle.

_____ 6. Clarence Berry left California to search for gold in the Yukon.

Extension: Ask students if they would have gone to the Klondike. Have them explain why they think they would or would not have gone.

Level 11/Unit 5
ORGANIZE INFORMATION:
Sequence of Events

Macmillan/McGraw-Hill

CLUES OF GOLD

When an unfamiliar word appears in a sentence, you can often figure out the meaning of the word by using context clues in the surrounding words and sentences.

Read each passage below from "Klondike Fever." Use context clues to figure out the meaning of each underlined word. Then write the meaning.

1. On board was the most precious <u>cargo</u> ever to enter the Seattle harbor—sixty-eight miners from the Klondike and more than two tons of gold.

Meaning: _____

2. It was two days earlier when the first of the gold ships had arrived in San Francisco, California. The <u>steamer</u> *Excelsior* had sailed into port, bringing its load of gold and the news that an even richer treasure ship was on its way to Seattle.

Meaning: _____

3. The big ship carefully pulled alongside the <u>wharf</u> and the gangplank was lowered.

Meaning: _____

4. When the first miner stepped into full view, the people stared in amazement. He heaved a buckskin bag to his shoulder and steadied the load. His face was lean and <u>weather-beaten</u>, lined with the strain of hard work and long Yukon winters.

Meaning: _____

5. The gold lay thick, so thick that Mrs. Berry—as *The Seattle Times* reported—could walk through the diggings and pick up <u>nuggets</u> "as easily as a hen picks up grains of corn in a barnyard." In one season she gathered more than $10,000 in nuggets during her occasional strolls through the claim.

Meaning: _____

6. By the winter of 1897, Canadian government officials had passed a law forbidding anyone from entering the gold fields without enough supplies to last an entire year. Once a <u>prospector</u> had spent $500 to buy a year's worth of goods for the Klondike, his load weighed about 2,000 pounds.

Meaning: _____

Level 11/Unit 5
**CONTEXT CLUES: Content-Area
and Specialized Vocabulary**

Extension: Have students circle the context clues they used to figure out the
meaning of each word.

133

MINING FOR THE MAIN IDEA

A **summary** is a brief statement that tells the main idea or point of a passage, story, or article. Summarizing can help you better understand the main ideas of a selection.

Read each passage below from "Klondike Fever." Then summarize the passage in your own words in one or two sentences.

1. The city of Seattle was usually still asleep at daybreak on weekend mornings, but this Saturday large crowds of people rushed to the downtown waterfront at dawn. They shouted excitedly to one another, pointed across the water, and craned their necks to

   see. The *Portland* was coming! _____

   _____

2. His face was lean and weather-beaten, lined with the strain of hard work and long Yukon winters. Behind him two men staggered down the ramp, each grasping the end of a sagging blanket. One after another they came, carrying old leather suitcases, pine

   boxes, and pickle jars—anything that would hold the heavy piles of gold. _____

   _____

3. The reason for this wild excitement was simple: The Klondike gold ships arrived during a time of terrible poverty for the United States. Thousands of businesses were closing,

   and millions of people had lost their jobs. _____

   _____

4. Firemen, store clerks, school teachers, lawyers, and doctors—workers from Seattle to San Francisco decided to trade their regular paychecks for picks and shovels. But the West Coast of the United States was not the only region to be turned upside down by the Yukon discoveries. "Klondike fever" had spread to cities and towns throughout the

   country—and throughout the world. _____

   _____

5. The stampeders often paused to watch street salesmen showing off the newest products designed for those traveling north. There were Klondike medicine chests,

   Klondike blankets, and Klondike electric gold pans. _____

   _____

134 **Extension:** Have students think up other items that might be sold as "Klondike" products if the gold rush were happening today.

Level 11/Unit 5
Summarize

5

Macmillan/McGraw-Hill

ARTICLE FEATURES

An article often includes photographs, maps, or captions that give additional information about the topic.

Look back at each photograph, map, or caption from "Klondike Fever" that is referred to below. Then answer each question.

1. What do you think the man shown on page 403 is doing? _____

2. Do you think this is a good photograph to show on the title page of the selection? Why or why not?_____

3. What is the importance of three men in the photos on page 404? _____

   _____

4. Do you think these portraits of the men were taken before or after their success? Why? _____

5. What information do you learn from the caption on page 405 that you couldn't learn by looking at the photograph itself? _____

   _____

6. How do you think the men were feeling when the photograph was taken?

   _____

7. Look at the map and caption on page 415. What are the names of the two routes?

   _____

8. Which route from Seattle to Dawson led goldseekers north of the Arctic Circle?

   _____

9. Look at the photograph and caption on page 417. How would you describe a gold miner's experience? _____

10. According to the caption, what expectations did newcomers have when arriving in Dawson?_____

   _____

10

Level 11/Unit 5
ORGANIZE INFORMATION: Photographs, Maps, Captions

Extension: Have students speculate which route from Seattle to Dawson took the longest. Have them use information on the map to explain their answers.

135

REASONS WHY

A **cause** is the reason why something happens, and an **effect** is the result, or what happens. An author often organizes the information in a nonfiction selection, such as "Klondike Fever," by cause and effect.

Complete the chart below by writing the missing cause or effect.

CAUSE	EFFECT
The *Portland* carried Klondike prospectors and tons of gold that they brought back from the Klondike.	**1.**
2.	After the arrival of the *Portland* and the *Excelsior,* thousands of people from the United States and many other countries decided to join the gold rush in the Klondike.
Each prospector needed the warmest clothes and most nourishing food money could buy to survive the harsh Arctic conditions.	**3.**
4.	Many dishonest merchants made money by selling worthless products.
Of the thousands of goldseekers who traveled to the Klondike, many of them stayed in the North and developed the frontier.	**5.**

136   **Extension:** Ask students what caused the Canadian government to forbid anyone from entering the gold fields without enough supplies to last one year.

Level 11/Unit 5
ORGANIZE INFORMATION:
Cause and Effect   5

Macmillan/McGraw-Hill

WHAT'S YOUR OPINION?

"Klondike Fever" contains many facts and opinions about the stampede to the Klondike. A **fact** is a statement that can be proved to be true by reference books, direct examination, or an expert. An **opinion** is a statement that tells how a person feels about something. An opinion cannot be proved true or false.

Read each passage below from "Klondike Fever." Underline one fact or one opinion in each passage. Then write *fact* or *opinion* on the line below to describe what you underlined.

1. On board was the most precious cargo ever to enter the Seattle harbor—sixty-eight miners from the Klondike and more than two tons of gold. _____

2. One of the reporters' favorite front page subjects was Clarence Berry, who had stepped off the *Portland* with $130,000 in gold nuggets. With his magnificent strength the broad-shouldered miner instantly became Seattle's hero. _____

3. Berry had set out from California to find his fortune three years earlier, leaving behind his childhood sweetheart and a bankrupt fruit farm. _____

4. "Klondike fever" had spread to cities and towns throughout the country—and throughout the world. In New York, 2,000 people tried to buy tickets for the Klondike before the news of the gold strikes was one day old. _____

5. One Klondiker, Arthur Dietz, stopped on the street to watch a salesman pour some yellow powder from a sack and make a plate of scrambled eggs. Dietz was so impressed that he bought 100 pounds of the evaporated eggs for him and his traveling companions. _____

6. One man set out for the Yukon as if he were taking a pleasant northern vacation. His outfit included thirty-two pairs of moccasins, one case of pipes, two Irish setters, a puppy, and a badminton set. _____

7. The newspapers were full of advertisements for strange new inventions that were "guaranteed" to make gold mining easier and pockets fuller. _____

8. Despite warnings, the excited stampeders did not seem to care whether their boats were seaworthy or not. The gold-crazed people pushed up the ramps, filling every available space on board. _____

Level 11/Unit 5
Fact and Opinion

Extension: Have students identify the facts and opinions in the two italicized paragraphs at the end of the selection.

Macmillan/McGraw-Hill

PROSPECTING FOR CLUES

Read each clue for the puzzle. Then write the answer to the clue in the correct place on the puzzle.

ACROSS

4. animals that were valuable possessions to goldseekers

5. the name of the ship that appeared in Seattle on July 17, 1897

7. one town on the Inside Passage Route

9. a period of economic hardship

10. kind of products sold by dishonest merchants

DOWN

1. what prospectors used to sift for gold

2. what the miners sought in the Klondike

3. the broad shouldered miner who was Seattle's hero

6. what one lady gathered during her occasional strolls through the claim

8. another name for someone who mines for gold

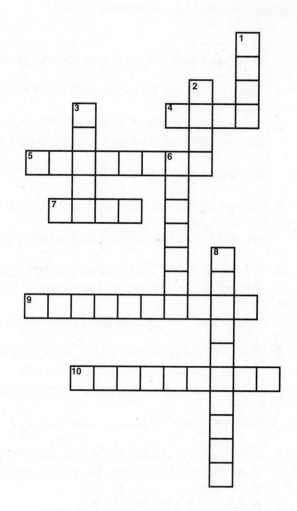

Extension: Have students list as many synonyms as possible for the words *gold miner*.

Level 11/Unit 5
Story Comprehension

 10

Look It Up!

As you know, a **card catalog** is a set of cards listing all the books in a library. Each alphabetized card catalog is made up of three different kinds of cards: author, title, and subject. **Author** cards list all books by the name of the author. **Title** cards list all books by the title. **Subject** cards list every nonfiction book by its subject.

Complete each line on the chart below. First, read what you are looking for in the left-hand column. Then, in the right-hand column, write what kind of card would be best to use: *author, title,* or *subject.*

WHAT YOU ARE LOOKING FOR	BEST CARD TO USE
a book about the Yukon Territory	1.
a book about gold	2.
the book *Klondike River Valley*	3.
a book by Delia Ray	4.
a book about the Klondike	5.
the book *Call of the Wild*	6.
a book about Clarence Berry	7.
the book *Gold! The Klondike Adventure*	8.
a book about the history of Dawson	9.
a book by Yukon Cornelius	10.

Name: _____   Date: _____

**My Adventures at the Center
of the Earth**
SELECTION VOCABULARY

WORDS IN CONTEXT

Supply the correct words to complete the paragraph.

specimen	prehistoric	subterranean	gigantic
disaster	admission	reptile	patio

This is a movie you have to see! It starts with three people sitting on a

_____ and eating breakfast. Then _____

strikes! A huge, scaly _____ appears from nowhere and

swallows the breakfast table. It's a _____ creature that's been

living underground for millions of years in some _____ cave.

One of the people is a scientist, and she's excited about the chance to study a

living _____ of an extinct dinosaur. She tries to find a place

large enough to hide this _____ dinosaur. The movie was

definitely worth the price of _____.

Macmillan/McGraw-Hill

Name: _____ Date: _____

My Adventures at the Center
of the Earth
COMPREHENSION: MAKE JUDGMENTS
AND DECISIONS

IN MY OPINION . . .

Think about each decision the main character made in "My Adventures at the Center of the Earth." Was each decision the right one to make? Tell why or why not.

1. The main character decided to dig a tunnel through the center of the earth. In your opinion, was this the right decision to make? Why or why not? _____

   _____

   _____

2. The main character chose her grandparents' backyard as the place to start digging. In your opinion, was this a good judgment to make? Why or why not? _____

   _____

   _____

3. The main character took her grandmother's diamond ring to cut the tunnel through the solid rock. In your opinion, was this the right decision to make? Why or why not?

   _____

   _____

   _____

4. The main character drank from the underground lake. In your opinion, was this a good judgment to make? Why or why not? _____

   _____

   _____

5. The main character decided to take the brontosaurus back to the surface. In your opinion, was this the right decision to make? Why or why not? _____

   _____

   _____

Level 11/Unit 5
Make Judgments and Decisions

Extension: Ask students to choose one of their explanations and underline the parts of their answer that are based on their own knowledge and experience.

141

Macmillan/McGraw-Hill

THAT'S RIDICULOUS!

Most stories have an overall **mood**, or feeling, that extends throughout the selection. The overall mood of "My Adventures at the Center of the Earth" could be described as playful or humorous.

Each passage below helps to create the humorous mood of the selection. Read each passage. Then tell what parts of the passage strike you as funny or silly.

1. People could travel to China through my tunnel on foot. I planned to charge admission to anyone who wanted to make the trip, except my family and my best friend at school. It was a sure thing!

   _____

   _____

2. Things looked bad. My project was on the edge of disaster. First of all, I could melt to death long before I reached China. Second of all, I would never be able to charge admission to go through such a dangerous place. And, finally, if I made a volcano appear in my grandparents' backyard, they would never let me sleep over again.

   _____

   _____

   _____

3. I hardly had enough strength to go on splitting rock. I wasn't sure I'd have enough strength to climb out of the hole.

   _____

4. First of all, I decided I would somehow have to tie the dinosaur up with my string. The animal had begun to trust me and soon followed behind, eating the bananas I left in his path.

   _____

5. Bronti lived for many years in my grandparents' backyard. He had a bad habit of eating all the figs. Grandmother complained because she couldn't use them anymore to make her favorite jam.

   _____

   _____

   _____

142   *Extension:* Ask students to circle the passage above that they think is the funniest of the five.

Level 11/Unit 5
ANALYZE STORY ELEMENTS: Mood   5

A CHANGE OF SCENE

In "My Adventures at the Center of the Earth," the author organizes the plot around a journey of the main character. The journey takes the main character through several settings.

Complete the story map below by telling what happened in each setting of the story.

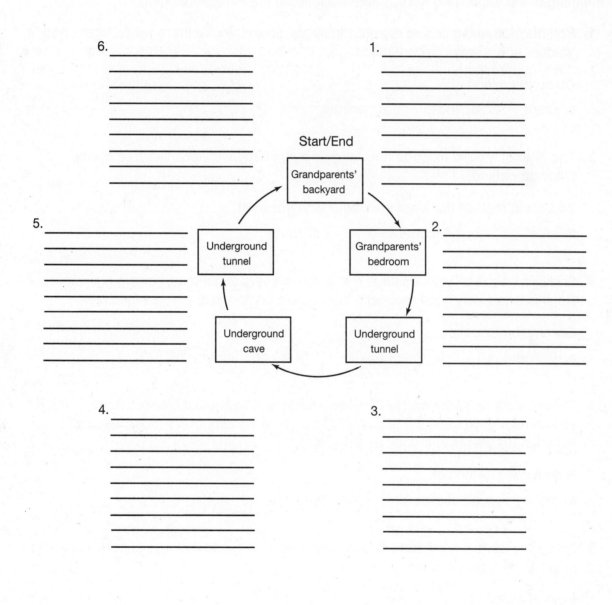

6. _____
_____
_____
_____
_____
_____
_____

1. _____
_____
_____
_____
_____
_____
_____

Start/End

Grandparents'
backyard

Underground
tunnel

Grandparents'
bedroom

5. _____
_____
_____
_____
_____
_____
_____

Underground
cave

Underground
tunnel

2. _____
_____
_____
_____
_____
_____
_____

4. _____
_____
_____
_____
_____
_____
_____
_____

3. _____
_____
_____
_____
_____
_____
_____
_____

Macmillan/McGraw-Hill

6

Level 11/Unit 5
ANALYZE STORY ELEMENTS:
Setting, Plot

Extension: Ask students whether the main character solved the problem that
began the story. Have them explain their answer on a separate sheet of paper.

143

A SUBTERRANEAN JOURNEY

As you read, you can use context clues to help you figure out the meanings of words that you don't know. **Context clues** are other words in a story that give hints to what unfamiliar words mean.

Read each passage from the selection below. Use context clues to help you figure out the meaning of the underlined word. Circle the letter of the correct meaning.

1. So I decided to dig behind my grandparents' house, where there was a big fig tree, a garden, and a small <u>chicory</u> patch.

   Chicory is a kind of _____.

   a. plant   **b.** rock   **c.** animal

2. The animal moved towards me. An <u>enormous</u> body with legs like tree trunks followed behind.

   You could replace the word *enormous* with the word _____.

   a. small   **b.** medium-sized   **c.** huge

3. Luckily it wasn't a Tyrannosaurus rex, which is a very dangerous, <u>carnivorous</u>, dinosaur. No, this was a very good-natured brontosaurus, content with eating vegetables.

   Carnivorous means _____.

   a. dangerous   **b.** meat-eating   **c.** good-natured

4. There I sank up to my waist in the high, thick, pink moss that blanketed the rocks. If you come to my house some day, I'll show you a handful of dry moss. I keep it between the pages of a book as a <u>souvenir</u>.

   A *souvenir* is a kind of _____.

   a. plant   **b.** bookmark   **c.** reminder

5. Below the earth's crust there is only molten rock, the kind that erupts from volcanoes in the form of <u>lava</u> and fire.

   Lava is a kind of _____.

   a. molten rock   **b.** volcano   **c.** fire

Macmillan/McGraw-Hill

A Different Sort of Trip

Think about what happens in "My Adventures at the Center of the Earth." Then complete the story chart below. Summarize the beginning, middle, and end of the story in a sentence or two.

Main character _____

Mood _____

Settings _____

Problem _____

Solution _____

Beginning _____

_____

Middle _____

_____

End _____

_____

_____

Extension: Have students imagine they are news reporters making a live broadcast from the backyard. Ask them to stand in front of the class and pretend they are interviewing the narrator and her grandmother.

Jurassic Giant

Read the information and study the pictures in the illustration below. Then answer each question.

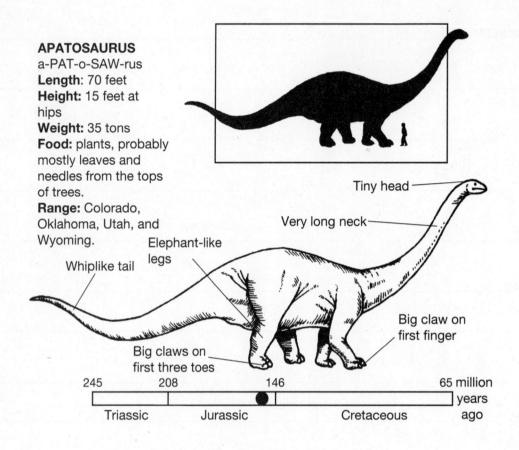

APATOSAURUS
a-PAT-o-SAW-rus
Length: 70 feet
Height: 15 feet at hips
Weight: 35 tons
Food: plants, probably mostly leaves and needles from the tops of trees.
Range: Colorado, Oklahoma, Utah, and Wyoming.

Tiny head

Very long neck

Elephant-like legs

Whiplike tail

Big claw on first finger

Big claws on first three toes

| 245 | 208 | 146 | 65 million |
| Triassic | Jurassic | Cretaceous | years ago |

1. How much did *Apatosaurus* weigh?_____

2. What can you learn from the small drawing in the box? _____

_____

3. What do the legs of *Apatosaurus* look like?_____

4. What can you learn about *Apatosaurus* from the time line at the bottom of the diagram?

_____

5. In what states did *Apatosaurus* range?_____

Extension: Ask students to look up similar information about *Tyrannosaurus rex.*
Have them write out answers on its height, weight, and eating habits.

Level 11/Unit 5
Graphic Aids: Diagrams

5

Macmillan/McGraw-Hill

WORDS IN CONTEXT

Supply the correct words to complete the sentences.

| pelted | interpret | stained | arrested |
| register | persuade | drizzling | certificates |

1. If it's raining steadily but not heavily, it's _____.

2. If someone is taken into custody by the police, that person has been

    _____.

3. If you explain what something means, you _____ it.

4. If you sign up to take a course, you _____ for it.

5. Documents that certify that something is true are called _____.

6. If you don't seek shelter during a hailstorm, you'll get _____ by hailstones.

7. If you convince someone that you are right, you _____ that person.

8. If your shirt gets spattered with ketchup, it will be _____.

WHEN ACTIONS SPEAK LOUDER THAN WORDS

You can learn about a character's personal traits and beliefs by paying attention to his or her words and actions.

Think back over "The Silent Lobby," and consider what Sylvester Saunders, Craig's father, does and says. Complete the web below by adding two important beliefs and two traits of the main character. Then list an event in the story that demonstrates each belief and trait. Include the setting for each event.

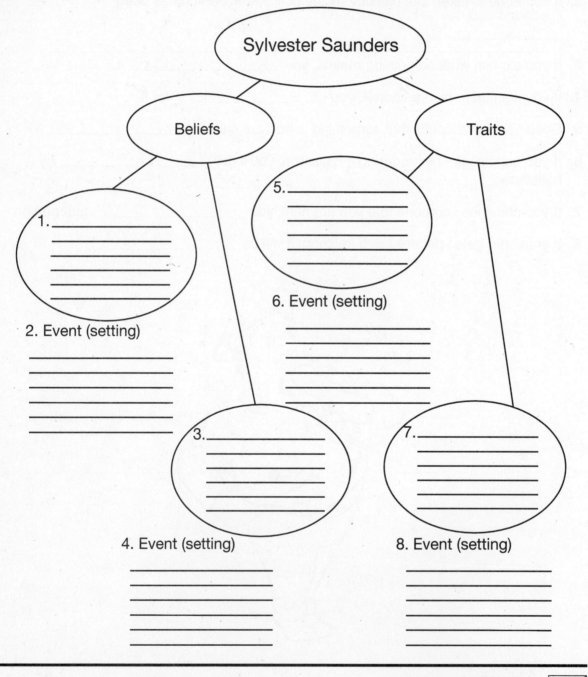

Sylvester Saunders

Beliefs

Traits

1. _____

2. Event (setting)
_____
_____
_____
_____

5. _____

6. Event (setting)
_____
_____
_____

3. _____

4. Event (setting)
_____
_____
_____
_____

7. _____

8. Event (setting)
_____
_____
_____
_____

Extension: Ask students to think about the events in the story that occur at the Capitol, in Washington, D.C. Have them list three settings where the action takes place.

Level 11/Unit 5
ANALYZE STORY ELEMENTS:
Character, Setting, Plot

8

Macmillan/McGraw-Hill

A PARTY IN THE LOBBY?

Sometimes a word can look familiar but have an unfamiliar meaning. To determine the correct meaning of the word, look for context clues in the nearby sentences and paragraphs.

Read each passage from "The Silent Lobby," and look at each underlined word. Then write the meaning.

1. Suddenly the bus stopped. Not again! We'd never make it now. Papa got out in the cold wind and icy drizzling rain and raised the <u>hood</u>.

_____

_____

2. Papa was getting ready to go into town to <u>register</u> to vote.

_____

_____

3. Members of the Freedom <u>Party</u> were like Papa—they didn't give up.

_____

_____

4. Why were they laughing? I knew that to <u>lobby</u> meant to try to get someone to decide for or against something. Yes, that was why we had come.

_____

_____

5. A little later, as we found seats in the <u>gallery</u>, Congressman Ford from the state of Michigan was speaking.

_____

_____

6. He did not want Mrs. Hamer and other fairly elected members of the Freedom Party seated in the <u>House</u>.

_____

_____

Macmillan/McGraw-Hill

Level 11/Unit 5
CONTEXT CLUES:
Multiple-Meaning Words

Extension: Ask students to look up the word *parliament*. Have them compare and contrast the English or Canadian Parliament with the United States Congress.

149

TAKING A STAND

List the pros and cons for each decision made by Sylvester Saunders in "The Silent Lobby." Then explain whether you would have made the same decision.

1. Sylvester decides to register to vote.

Pros _____

_____

Cons _____

_____

2. Would you have made the same decision? Why or why not?

_____

3. Sylvester decides to take his eleven-year-old son with him to lobby for voting rights in Washington, D.C.

Pros _____

_____

Cons _____

_____

4. Would you have made the same decision? Why or why not?

_____

5. Sylvester and the others in the group from Mississippi decide to stand silently in the tunnel as members of Congress walk by.

Pros _____

_____

Cons _____

_____

6. Would you have made the same decision? Why or why not?

_____

150

Extension: To help students put Sylvester's first decision in historical context, have them list the time and place in which the story takes place and one voting law that affected blacks in this setting.

Level 11/Unit 5
Make Judgments and Decisions

6

STRUGGLING FOR FREEDOM

In "The Silent Lobby," Sylvester Saunders reveals his determination and strong beliefs through his words. As you review or reread the selection, record what the character says in response to each event below.

1. Sylvester's wife asks, "Why can't you just forget about this voting business and let us live in peace?"

Sylvester replies, _____

_____

2. Sylvester's boss warns Papa that he should not try to register to vote.

Sylvester says, _____

_____

3. A man in the crowd at the Capitol asks, "What brings you all to the District?"

Sylvester answers,_____

_____

4. Someone in the crowd tells the Mississippi group that they are too late to lobby. The group gets back on the bus to talk.

Sylvester says,_____

_____

Now, make predictions. Think about Sylvester Saunders's words and how the members of Congress voted after noticing the silent lobby.

5. What do you think Sylvester and his son Craig will do in the future about laws that keep African Americans from voting?

_____

_____

6. What effect might the "silent lobby" have had on members of Congress in future votes?

_____

_____

Macmillan/McGraw-Hill

6   Level 11/Unit 5
Make, Confirm, or Revise Predictions

Extension: Ask students if they were surprised by the result of the vote. Did they expect the silent lobby to make a difference? Have them explain their answer on a separate sheet of paper.

151

MAKING A DIFFERENCE

Complete the chart to show the cause-and-effect links between events in "The Silent Lobby."

Cause	Effect
1. _____ _____	Sylvester Saunders loses his job.
The Freedom Party registers people to vote without poll taxes or literacy tests.	2. _____ _____ _____
3. _____ _____ _____	Three white men are declared winners in the election.
The governor ignores petitions asking him to count the votes of black people.	4. _____ _____ _____
5. _____ _____ _____	The doorman lets the Mississippi group into the tunnel below the Capitol.
6. _____ _____ _____	Members of Congress cast 148 votes in favor of seating representatives elected by the Freedom Party.

Extension: Ask students to draw an arrow from each cause to each effect.

LOSING AND WINNING

Think about the events in "The Silent Lobby." Then complete the story chart below.

Main characters   1. _____

Other characters   2. _____

Narrator   3. _____

Time   4. _____

Place   5. _____

_____

Main problem   6. _____

_____

_____

Solution (plan)   7. _____

_____

_____

Events leading to the climax   8. _____

_____

_____

_____

_____

Ending   9. _____

_____

_____

_____

Message of the story   10. _____

Macmillan/McGraw-Hill

Extension: Ask students to make a judgment about the ending of the story. Do they think that the silent lobby had been worth the effort? Why or why not? Have them respond on a separate sheet of paper.

THE STATE OF THE STATE

Study the map of Mississippi and information block from an atlas of the United
States. Then answer each question.

1. What three major rivers of Mississippi are shown on the map?_____

   _____

2. In what year did Mississippi become a state? _____

3. What two highways meet in Jackson, the capital? _____

4. What is the height of Woodall Mountain, the highest point in the state? _____

5. What state borders Mississippi on the east? _____

6. Which of the two largest cities is located on the Gulf of Mexico? _____

154 **Extension:** Ask students to highlight the Mississippi River on the map with a felt-tip marker or colored pen.

Level 11/Unit 5
Reference Sources: Atlas

Macmillan/McGraw-Hill

UNIT VOCABULARY REVIEW

Underline the words your teacher says.

1. advantage	2. doubt	3. disaster	4. pellet
adventure	drought	disease	pelted
advance	draft	dissatisfied	belted

5. assessment	6. rustle	7. gigantic	8. personal
assembled	restless	giant	persuade
resembled	roasted	giggling	persist

9. poetry	10. bearded	11. repeal	12. regret
powerful	boarded	reptile	regular
poverty	bored	repair	register

13. guarded	14. capturing	15. prepositions	16. stand
guaranteed	capable	prehistoric	stunned
guided	capital	preheated	stained

17. milliliter	18. scratch	19. specific	20. certificates
millionaire	snitch	spaceman	certainty
military	scrape	specimen	caretakers

21. perspective	22. adviser	23. pattern	24. dizzy
prosperous	admonish	patty	drizzling
prospector	admission	patio	dozing

25. bashful	26. subtraction	27. arranged	28. interest
basement	subtitle	artery	interpret
basketball	subterranean	arrested	interrupt

WORDS IN CONTEXT

Label each sentence *True* or *False*. If a sentence is false, explain why.

1. If you think carefully before answering, you answer *automatically*.

_____

2. Information you can depend on to be true is *reliable* information.

_____

3. If you drove slowly and carefully on a winding road, you would have *swerved* often.

_____

4. If you give the wrong answer, you answer *incorrectly*.

_____

5. If you believe things without question, you are *skeptical*.

_____

6. Things you see and take note of are *observations*.

_____

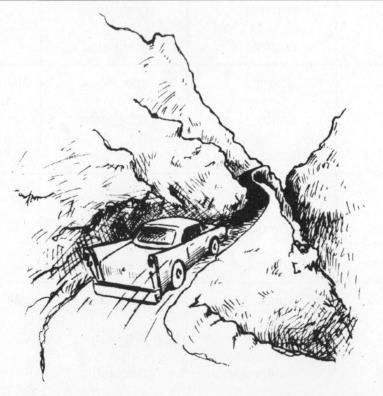

PARTS OF THE WHOLE

Some nonfiction selections are made up of several sections. If you summarize each part, you will have a better understanding of the selection as a whole. Remember that when you summarize you briefly retell the most important ideas in your own words, leaving out minor details. Summarize each section of "How to Think Like a Scientist."

First section (two boys and a snake) _____

_____

_____

_____

Second section (events in the Murphys' yard) _____

_____

_____

_____

_____

Third section (fish in a bowl) _____

_____

_____

_____

_____

Fourth section (the math assignment) _____

_____

_____

_____

_____

Main idea (summarize the most important idea in the selection) _____

_____

_____

Level 11/Unit 6
Summarize

Extension: Ask students to add a short title to each summary they wrote. (Tell them to avoid the exact phrases given in parentheses above as content reminders.)

QUESTIONS EVERY DAY

A generalization is a broad statement based on several facts or examples.

The stories in "How to Think Like a Scientist" give examples of how we answer questions. Think about what happened in each story. List three ways that a person can go wrong when answering a question. Then use your examples to complete two generalizations about scientific thinking.

Three Ways a Person Can Go Wrong When Answering Questions		
1. _____ _____ _____ _____ _____ _____	2. _____ _____ _____ _____ _____ _____	3. _____ _____ _____ _____ _____ _____

Generalization

4. When answering questions, you should _____

_____

5. Good scientists always _____

Extension: Ask students to think up an example, similar to the stories in the selection, to support their last generalization.

AGREE OR DISAGREE?

Scientists often test the judgments they make. These tests are called experiments.

Read the following passage and answer the questions.

"There's a ghost in our new house!" Charlie said. "I saw it open the attic door!"

"Now wait a minute, Charlie," his big sister Camilla said. "There aren't any such things as ghosts."

"But I saw it," Charlie insisted. "The door opened and no one was there."

"Let's go check it out," Camilla said. The hardwood floor creaked a little as they walked along the hallway.

The door to the attic sat ajar, open only a little. Camilla shut it, but had to push against it to hear the "click" of its latch.

She pulled on it. It didn't move.

"Charlie," Camilla said, "walk along the hallway, just as you did when the door opened." Charlie did so but nothing happened. "Charlie," Camilla said, "try it again."

Charlie walked down the hall. The floor creaked a little right by the door, and "click," the door opened.

"Ghosts!" Charlie cried.

"Hardly," Camilla said, looking behind the door. She closed it and asked Charlie to try it again. After a number of times walking past the door, Camilla proved to Charlie that if he walked past it just right, his weight shifted against the creaky floor to allow the door to pop open.

1. What happened that scared Charlie? _____

2. Why did Charlie believe a ghost opened the door? _____

3. Why didn't Camilla believe Charlie's idea about a ghost?_____

_____

4. Charlie and Camilla both made observations. How did Camilla test Charlie's observation?

_____

5. What is the name of the method Camilla used to make her test?_____

_____

5
Level 11/Unit 6
Make Judgments and Decisions

Extension: Ask students to discuss a recent decision and whether or not it turned
out as they hoped it would.

159

ANSWERING CAREFULLY

The author of "How to Think Like a Scientist" asks questions for which there are correct answers and offers reasons why people give incorrect answers. Think about what you learned in "How to Think Like a Scientist." Use that information to complete the chart below.

Question	Correct Answer	Reason for Incorrect Answer
1. _____ _____ _____ _____	2. _____ _____ _____ _____	3. _____ _____ _____ _____
4. _____ _____ _____ _____	5. _____ _____ _____ _____	6. _____ _____ _____ _____
7. _____ _____ _____ _____	8. _____ _____ _____ _____	9. _____ _____ _____ _____

Author's purpose for writing the selection

10. _____

_____

_____

Extension: Ask students to recall their reactions when they read the stories about the three questions above. In which story did the correct answer surprise them the most? Have them circle the related question.

Level 11/Unit 6
Story Comprehension

10

HAVE YOU READ A MAGAZINE TODAY?

Look over the contents page of a science magazine below. Then answer each question.

SCIENCE NOW

March 1997
Vol. 68, No.4

Spinner in the Lab   23
How can a spider's thread help you see
through a microscope? Dr. Leroy Biggs
explains.

A New Nebula   28
From Science Fair to College Classroom   33
Exploring a Mangrove Swamp   40
Biotechnology: What's Now, What's Next   46
Turn Left at Cuba: How Birds Migrate   51

DEPARTMENTS
From Our Readers   9
Science Update   12
Bookmarks   53
Opportunities for Young Scientists   57

STAFF
Publisher: Reginald C. Brown
Managing Editor: Beverly Scully
Associate Editor: Ken Bettelmann
Copy Editor: Wanida Deksakulthorn
Art Director: Paul Faiola
Advertising Director: Mary Smith-Otting
Circulation: Joseph Yagoda

---

1. What is the name of the magazine? _____

2. How often is it published? _____

3. Who is the managing editor? _____

4. What do you think you would find if you turned to "From Our Readers"?

   _____

5. What heading identifies features that appear in every issue of the magazine?

   _____

6. Which article is about one kind of environment? _____

7. What is the cover story about? _____

8. Which article might be of special interest to science students who plan to go to college?

   _____

Macmillan/McGraw-Hill

8

Level 11/Unit 6
Reference Sources:
Newspapers and Magazines

Extension: Ask students to discuss their favorite magazines. Do they use them as information resources? Have them explain.

161

WORDS IN CONTEXT

Supply the correct words to complete the paragraph.

fossils   revealed   conceal   nimble

attract   digesting   strides   markings

    The paleontologist sat quietly in her tent _____ her

midday meal and examining the _____ she had unearthed that

morning. Suddenly, she saw her young helper running toward the tent and

shouting to _____ her attention. The young man

_____ that he had been badly frightened by an animal with

unusual _____. The scientist went off to have a look for

herself, walking with long, determined _____. When she saw

the familiar creature with the white stripe on its back, her

_____ mind identified it at once. She made no effort to

_____ her eagerness to get as far away as she could, as fast

as her feet would carry her.

WHEN DINOSAURS RULED THE EARTH

A **fact** is a statement that careful investigation can prove to be true. A **nonfact** is a statement that can be proved false. There are many facts and nonfacts floating around about dinosaurs. Use the information you have learned in "The News About Dinosaurs" to label the following statements as *facts* or *nonfacts*.

1. The name *dinosaur* means "terrible lizard." _____

2. All dinosaurs were slow and clumsy. _____

3. Some small meat-eating dinosaurs could run very fast. _____

4. Sauropods lived in the water. _____

5. *Nanotyrannus* was a giant version of *Tyrannosaurus rex.* _____

6. *Deinonychus* was dug up in Montana. _____

7. *Albertosaurus* was strictly a plant-eater. _____

8. Benjamin Waterhouse Hawkins was a painter who painted dinosaurs.

   _____

9. The biggest dinosaurs were the plant-eating sauropods. _____

10. Dinosaurs were all plain gray in color. _____

Level 11/Unit 6
Fact and Nonfact

Extension: Have students look for other examples of facts and nonfacts in this selection. Remind them that statements of nonfact will be those which the author says that modern research has refuted.

163

THE NEWS IN BRIEF

For each topic below, summarize what people used to believe about dinosaurs in the past and what they believe today.

TOPIC	
OLD BELIEFS	**NEW BELIEFS**
Movement of Dinosaurs	
1. _____ _____ _____ _____ _____ _____	2. _____ _____ _____ _____ _____ _____
Color of Dinosaurs	
3. _____ _____ _____ _____ _____	4. _____ _____ _____ _____ _____
Sauropods	
5. _____ _____ _____ _____ _____	6. _____ _____ _____ _____ _____

Macmillan/McGraw-Hill

164   **Extension:** Have students summarize other parts of the selection.

Level 11/Unit 6
Summarize

6

DINOSAURS CAUSED A BIG EFFECT ON PLANET EARTH!

Complete the chart below by writing in the missing cause or effect.

CAUSE	EFFECT
1. _____ _____ _____	They found many different kinds and sizes of dinosaurs.
Dinosaurs walked in mud or wet sand.	2. _____ _____ _____
3. _____ _____ _____	We may never know what color dinosaurs were.
Sauropods needed to reach into treetops for food.	4. _____ _____ _____
5. _____ _____ _____	Scientists think that the parts of dinosaurs' brains that control the senses were highly developed.
Meat-eaters may have had markings of various colors.	6. _____ _____ _____

Level 11/Unit 6
ORGANIZE INFORMATION:
Cause and Effect

Extension: Ask students what they think might have caused the extinction of dinosaurs.

165

Macmillan/McGraw-Hill

DETAILS ABOUT DINOSAURS

Listed below are a number of the author's main ideas about dinosaurs. For each main idea, give details from the selection that support it.

Dinosaur bones were discovered in the 1800s.

1. _____

   _____

2. _____

   _____

3. _____

   _____

Some dinosaurs were plant-eaters.

4. _____

   _____

5. _____

   _____

6. _____

   _____

7. _____

Some dinosaurs were meat-eaters.

8. _____

   _____

9. _____

   _____

10. _____

   _____

166   **Extension:** Have the students identify another main idea about dinosaurs and list some supporting details.

Level 11/Unit 6
ORGANIZE INFORMATION:
Main Idea and Supporting Details

10

SOLVE THE PUZZLE OF THE DINOSAURS!

Use the clues given below to fill in the crossword puzzle about dinosaurs.

DOWN

1. This 30-foot long dinosaur had a snout like a crocodile's.

_____

3. The biggest dinosaurs belonged to this group of plant-eaters.

_____

ACROSS

2. This giant, 72-foot long dinosaur was named for the place in China where it was discovered.

_____

4. The name of this dinosaur means "pygmy tyrant."

_____

5. This Montana dinosaur had a big claw on each hind foot.

_____

Level 11/Unit 6
Story Comprehension

Extension: Have students add additional words associated with dinosaurs to the above puzzle, or have them make up a new puzzle based on this selection.

167

Macmillan/McGraw-Hill

Name: _____ Date: _____

THE BIG PICTURE FOR A BIG CREATURE

Charts arrange information so that it is easier to understand. Look over the chart below, and answer the questions.

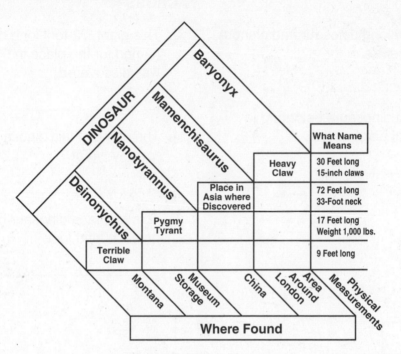

1. Which dinosaur was found in Montana?

_____

2. Which dinosaur was found in China?

_____

3. What dinosaur name means "heavy claw"?

_____

4. What were the physical measurements of Mamenchisaurus?

_____

5. Which dinosaur has a name that means "pygmy tyrant"?

_____

6. Which dinosaur was only 9 feet long?

_____

168 Extension: Have students add information about another dinosaur mentioned in the selection.

Level 11/Unit 6
Graphic Aids: Charts and Tables

Macmillan/McGraw-Hill

WORDS IN CONTEXT

Complete each sentence with a vocabulary word.

microscope   rival

gravity   concentrated

expenses   reduced

1. If all the light is focused on one point, the light is _____ there.

2. Someone who is always competing with you for something is your

   _____.

3. The force that causes a pencil to drop when you let go of it is _____.

4. If you can see tiny organisms moving about in clear water, you are probably looking

   through a _____.

5. When something shrinks, its size is _____.

6. The money you spend on a trip could be called your travel _____.

SCIENCE SLEUTHING

The problem in each Einstein Anderson story is a puzzle. Einstein gives readers the scientific information they need to solve each puzzle. In the charts below, tell what the problem, or puzzle, was in each story. Word the problem as a question. Then complete each chart.

The Incredible Shrinking Machine

Problem:	Solution:
1. _____	2. _____
_____	_____
_____	_____
_____	_____
_____	_____
_____	_____
_____	_____

Science knowledge needed for solution:

3. _____

The Impossible Trick

Problem:	Solution:
4. _____	5. _____
_____	_____
_____	_____
_____	_____
	_____

Science knowledge needed for solution:

6. _____

_____

170   **Extension:** Have students draw a picture to illustrate one of their explanations above.

Level 11/Unit 6
ORGANIZE INFORMATION:
Problem and Solution   6

Macmillan/McGraw-Hill

Information Sifting

The important information in the stories about Einstein Anderson is the information that you need to solve the puzzles. Read each sentence below from the Einstein Anderson stories. Mark an *X* next to each sentence that contains important information.

The Incredible Shrinking Machine

_____ **1.** The early-morning sun shone directly on the yellow door and made it look almost like gold.

_____ **2.** Einstein noticed that the single room they entered had no other doors and only one small window.

_____ **3.** You can see that it [the stone table] is too big to pass through the door or the window.

_____ **4.** They used a microscope to look at the protozoa in a drop of pond water.

The Impossible Trick

_____ **5.** The next day the committee was giving their ideas about a booth for their class.

_____ **6.** All you have to do is bend over and touch your toes without bending your knees.

_____ **7.** Your feet have to remain against the wall as you bend.

_____ **8.** I'm sorry I called you a noodle head yesterday.

Level 11/Unit 6
Important and Unimportant Information

Extension: Ask students to find one more sentence in each of the stories that contains important information. Have them write the sentence at the end of the appropriate section above.

171

Macmillan/McGraw-Hill

QUITE A CHARACTER

In the chart, write four characteristics of Einstein Anderson. Then tell what information from the two stories supports each conclusion about his character.

Characteristics	Supporting Information
1. _____	2. _____ _____ _____ _____ _____
3. _____	4. _____ _____ _____ _____ _____
5. _____	6. _____ _____ _____ _____
7. _____	8. _____ _____ _____ _____ _____

Extension: Ask students if Margaret Michaels shares any of Einstein's traits. Have them place a check mark next to each trait they listed that could also apply to Margaret.

Macmillan/McGraw-Hill

PUZZLING SITUATIONS

At certain points in a story, you will probably find yourself trying to predict what will happen next. As you continue to read, you can confirm your prediction, or find out if it was correct.

Answer each question below.

1. Margaret tells Einstein she has a science puzzle to show him at Aunt Bess's. What

kind of puzzle did you think she might have? _____

_____

2. What was the puzzle? _____

_____

3. What did you think was the solution to the puzzle? _____

_____

4. What was the key to solving the puzzle? _____

_____

5. Einstein said he could come up with an idea for a science booth that would be fun.

What kind of booth idea did you think he might offer? _____

_____

6. What was Einstein's idea? _____

_____

_____

7. What did you predict would happen when Pat tried out Einstein's idea? _____

_____

_____

8. What scientific idea was Einstein's trick based on? _____

_____

Level 11/Unit 6
Make, Confirm, or Revise Predictions

Extension: Ask students to circle any predictions they made that turned out to
be correct.

173

JUST THE FACTS, PLEASE

A statement or idea that can be proven to be true is a **fact**. A statement or an idea that can be proven to be false is called a **nonfact**.

Read each sentence and decide whether it states a fact or a nonfact. Write *F* if it is a fact and *N* if it is a nonfact.

_____   **1.** The sun rises in the east in the morning and sets in the west in the evening.

_____   **2.** There is a machine that can shrink a stone table to the size of an atom.

_____   **3.** Sunlight strikes different sides of a building at different times of day.

_____   **4.** Only adults can touch their toes when they stand with their feet and back against a wall.

_____   **5.** Strange things always happen in buildings with yellow doors.

_____   **6.** In order to touch your toes, your center of gravity must be directly over your feet.

174   **Extension:** Ask students to circle the facts that tell them something about the movement of the sun.   Level 11/Unit 6
Fact and Nonfact

Macmillan/McGraw-Hill

USING YOUR NOODLE

Think about the two Einstein Anderson stories. Then complete the story charts below.

The Incredible Shrinking Machine

Main characters	_____ _____
Plot event leading to problem	_____ _____
Problem	_____ _____
Science idea used to solve problem	_____ _____

The Impossible Trick

Main characters	_____ _____
Plot event leading to problem	_____ _____
Problem	_____ _____
Science idea used to solve problem	_____ _____

8

Level 11/Unit 6
Story Comprehension

Extension: Ask students to come up with their own titles for each story and write them at the top of each chart.

175

A BUSY SCHEDULE

Look over the calendar below. Then answer each question about the activities recorded on the calendar.

JUNE

Sunday	Monday	Tuesday	Wednesday	Thursday	Friday	Saturday
				1 Swimming lesson, 10:00	**2** Visit Grandpa ←——————————→	**3**
4 Youth choir on radio, WRDM, 2:00	**5** Swim lesson, 10:00	**6** Last day to sign up for basketball camp	**7**	**8** Swimming lesson, 10:00	**9** Kwame's birthday party, 7:30	**10** Litter clean-up, Riverside Park, 10:00–12:00 / Help Ben with bike repair, 2:00
11	**12** Swimming lesson, 10:00	**13**	**14** "Otters," Nature, Ch. 34, 7:30	**15** Swimming lesson, 10:00	**16** Close-out sale at Grumman's Sporting Goods	**17** Early Girls concert, Wilson Hall, 8:00

1. What activity takes place on June 2 and 3? _____

2. What activity happens each Monday and Thursday? _____

3. When is the litter clean-up at Riverside Park? _____

4. If you were looking for a pair of basketball shoes at a good price, what date might you want to circle? _____

5. When and where is the Early Girls concert? _____

6. What might you want to listen to on the radio on June 4? _____

Extension: Ask students to circle the date of Kwame's birthday party on the calendar.

Level 11/Unit 6
Graphic Aids: Schedules

6

Macmillan/McGraw-Hill

WORDS IN CONTEXT

Supply the correct words to complete the paragraph.

invading   enchantment

universe   flailed

cramped   alien

Keisha stood by the window, massaging her _____ neck.

In the bright light of morning, the world seemed like a magic place, a place of

_____, where anything could happen. _____

armies of fairies might sprinkle you with fairy dust. Swarms of shimmering

butterflies might circle around your head until you _____ your

arms to drive them away. An _____ might carry you off to

another corner of the _____. Dawn and a sleepless night

made the world seem alive with strange possibilities.

THE SEESAW EFFECT

Cause and effect are like the movements of a seesaw. When *Cause* pushes down one end, the other end, *Effect,* must go up. Fill in the chart below by completing the sentences.

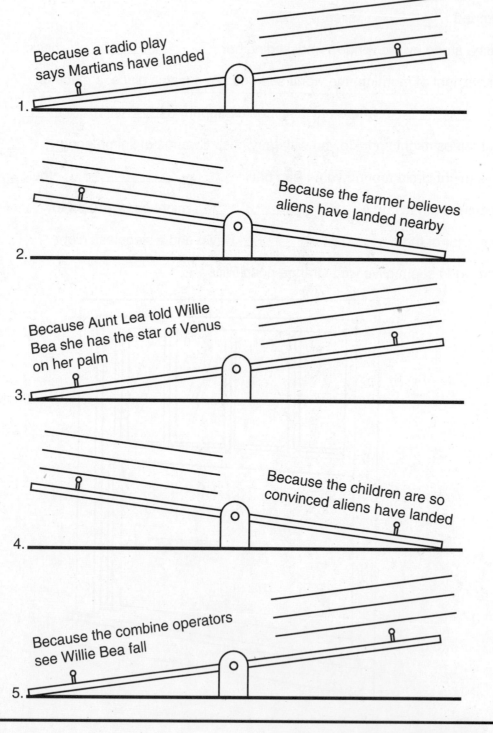

1. Because a radio play says Martians have landed

2. Because the farmer believes aliens have landed nearby

3. Because Aunt Lea told Willie Bea she has the star of Venus on her palm

4. Because the children are so convinced aliens have landed

5. Because the combine operators see Willie Bea fall

Macmillan/McGraw-Hill

Extension: Have students discuss why it is important to remain calm in an emergency, such as a fire. What would be the effect if everyone panicked?

JUDGING A CHARACTER'S ACTIONS

Think about the decisions made by the main character in "Willie Bea and the Time the Martians Landed." Answer each question below. Explain your answers.

1. Willie Bea decided to go out and look for aliens in the night. In your opinion, would it be wise to go out at night to look for creatures that could be dangerous? Why or why not?

   _____

   _____

2. Willie Bea decided to travel across the countryside on stilts. In your opinion, was this the right decision to make? Why or why not?

   _____

   _____

3. Willie Bea decided to take Toughy Clay with her on her search for aliens. In your opinion, was it wise of her not to go alone? Why or why not?

   _____

   _____

4. Willie Bea went off toward the Kelly house, but she did not go up to the door to speak to the people. Would it have been wise for her to talk to them? Why or why not?

   _____

   _____

5. Willie Bea heard on the radio that aliens had landed, and she believed it. In your opinion, was this the right conclusion to draw? Why or why not?

   _____

   _____

5

Level 11/Unit 6
Make Judgments and Decisions

Extension: Have students discuss different types of programs, such as news broadcasts and historical reenactments. Ask if it is ever hard to tell whether a story is fact or fiction.

179

Monsters in the Cornfield?

Read each passage from the selection. Then answer each question.

Toughy Clay didn't dare turn around to check their backs, for fear he would see something beyond belief and fall. "You ever think what's gone happen if one of us fall off these dang stilts?" he whispered loudly to Willie Bea.

1. How do you think Toughy Clay is feeling in this passage?_____

_____

_____

"Don' chu know they is Martians spreadin' they sin all over this land?" said the farmer. "Get on in your home!"

2. Why does the farmer tell Willie Bea and Toughy Clay to go home?_____

_____

_____

Something struck her a glancing blow on the forehead.
    All went dark for Willie Bea. The dark filled with glowing comets and stars. Great planets of Venus and Mars. All such colors of worlds, pumpkin yellow and orange in a Halloween universe.

3. What do you think happened to Willie Bea in this scene?_____

_____

4. Why do you think she saw stars and planets and pumpkin colors in her mind?

_____

_____

_____

Willie Bea saw a man in the light. He knelt beside her. "Did the combines scare you, child? We might've run you over!"

5. Who is the man? _____

_____

6. How do you think the farmer is feeling? Explain. _____

_____

Extension: Pose this question: If you had been in the cornfield, would you have concluded that the combines were aliens, as Willie Bea and Toughy did? Have students explain their answer on a separate sheet of paper.

180

Level 11/Unit 6
Draw Conclusions

6

Outlandish Aliens

Read each passage from "Willie Bea and the Time the Martians Landed." Use context clues to help you figure out the meaning of each underlined word. Circle the letter of the correct answer.

1. Toughy Clay didn't dare turn around to check their backs, for fear he would see something beyond belief and fall. . . . "The evening star of Venus could be falling down on us this very minute," she told him.

   "You think so?" he said <u>anxiously</u>.

   a. quickly   **b.** worriedly

   c. loudly   **d.** boldly

2. Suddenly, there was a burst of flames close to a fence in a field they were passing. The flames grew rapidly into a huge <u>bonfire</u>.

   a. burning building   **b.** large outdoor fire

   c. campfire   **d.** forest fire

3. Willie Bea and Toughy went, striding as fast as their legs and arms <u>propelling</u> the stilts would take them, their capes bouncing.

   a. holding still   **b.** waving

   c. pushing forward   **d.** breaking

4. Willie Bea shifted, too. But she was better at balancing than Toughy was. Just arm pressure and <u>flexing</u> leg muscles was all that was necessary.

   a. tightening and loosening **b.** holding stiffly

   c. keeping loose   **d.** jerking violently

5. The great black dark that moved was one of the monsters. It was a rolling, ear-splitting, <u>outlandish</u> alien. And huge.

   a. familiar   **b.** plain and common

   c. faraway   **d.** very strange

5

Level 11/Unit 6
CONTEXT CLUES: Unfamiliar Words

Extension: In each sentence, have students circle any context clues to the meaning of the underlined word.

181

A FANTASTIC IMAGINATION

Complete the sentences below. Look back over the selection to help you.

1. In the beginning, Willie Bea and Toughy Clay are _____
_____.

↓

2. They are surprised by the sight of _____.

↓

3. A man with a shotgun _____.

↓

4. Then they follow a gravel road and pass _____.

↓

5. In the cornfields nearby, they hear _____.

↓

6. Then they see _____, which they think are _____.

↓

7. Frightened and excited, Willie Bea _____.

↓

8. Her mind goes dark, and she imagines _____
_____.

↓

9. One of the farmers _____.

↓

10. Still confused, Willie Bea imagines _____.

182   **Extension:** Ask students to circle the events that make up the beginning, middle, and end of the selection.

Level 11/Unit 6
ORGANIZE INFORMATION:
Sequence of Events

10

FANTASY AND FACTS

Think about what happens in "Willie Bea and the Time the Martians Landed." Then complete the story map below.

Questions	Answers
1. What is the setting?	_____
2. Who are the main characters?	_____
3. How does the selection begin?	_____ _____ _____ _____
4. What events lead to the climax?	_____ _____ _____ _____ _____ _____ _____
5. How does the selection end?	_____ _____ _____ _____ _____

Level 11/Unit 6
Story Comprehension

Extension: Have students consider whether Willie Bea would have gone on her adventure if Aunt Leah had not told her about the palm of Venus. Would the selection have been as interesting?

FAIR TIME

Look over the fair schedule below. Then answer each question about the activities listed.

County Fair Events

THURSDAY

8:00–10:00	Junior Market Lamb Judging, Cooper Arena
10:00–12:00	Senior Market Lamb Judging, Cooper Arena
12:00–1:00	Juggling Performance, Fair Pavilion
1:00–3:00	Dairy Goat Judging, Sheep and Goat Barn
3:00	Antique Tractor Parade, Grandstand
4:00	Pie-Eating Contest, Multipurpose Building
5:00–7:00	Tractor Pull, Grandstand
8:00	Concert, Wells Fargo Band, Grandstand

FRIDAY

8:00–10:00	Swine Judging, Cooper Arena
10:00–12:00	Rabbit Judging, Rabbit Barn
12:00–1:00	Cooking with Pork Demonstration, Multipurpose Building
1:00–3:00	4-H Booth Judging, Exhibits Building A
3:00	Milking Demonstration, Dairy Barn
4:00	Square Dance, Fair Pavilion
5:00–7:00	Pony Races, Grandstand
8:00	Demolition Derby, Grandstand

1. On what day and at what time is the rabbit judging? _____

2. Where should you go to see the swine judging? _____

3. On which afternoon is the square dance? _____

4. When and where is the milking demonstration? _____

5. What event occurs at 8:00 Friday night? _____

6. Where will the pie-eating contest be held? _____

184 Extension: Ask students to circle the time and underline the place for the juggling performance.

Level 11/Unit 6
Graphic Aids: Schedules   6

Macmillan/McGraw-Hill

UNIT VOCABULARY REVIEW

Underline the words your teacher says.

1. obstructions	**2.** attempt	**3.** concentrated	**4.** camped
observations	attack	concertmaster	crumpled
obvious	attract	concentric	cramped
5. sweated	**6.** marbles	**7.** gravy	**8.** encounter
swept	markets	gravity	enclosure
swerved	markings	gravelly	enchantment
9. autographical	**10.** revealed	**11.** microspore	**12.** university
automatically	reversed	microscope	unity
automobile	reviewed	microsecond	universe
13. reliable	**14.** consider	**15.** reduced	**16.** alone
relinquish	conceal	redeemed	align
religious	concern	redhead	alien
17. incorrectly	**18.** diverting	**19.** rival	**20.** flamed
incompletely	digging	regal	flailed
incredibly	digesting	raving	flaked
21. skeleton	**22.** noble	**23.** experts	**24.** invading
skeptical	number	expenses	invention
sketchbook	nimble	expires	invalid
25. strife	**26.** fosters		
strikes	fossils		
strides	fortunes